LIFE AT ITS BEST

LIFE AT ITS BEST

by

Ellen G. White

PACIFIC PRESS PUBLISHING ASSOCIATION

Mountain View, California ☆ ☆ Omaha, Nebraska

Oshawa, Ontario

Copyright © 1964, by
Pacific Press Publishing Association
Newsprint edition printed in Canada 1979

Library of Congress Catalog Card Number 64-8510

A WORD TO THE READER

Life offers many treasures, the most valuable of which are health, a happy home, true friends, peace of mind, and peace with God. All of these riches may be yours regardless of your position in life. You may enjoy life to the full—life at its very best.

But there are certain considerations. If you are to benefit fully from life's best gifts you should understand and accept a few basic principles. These time-honored principles, as set forth in this volume, have opened the door of hope to millions to whom they have been presented from the public platform in many lands, or through the printed page in the world's leading languages.

Life at Its Best represents major selections from the book *The Ministry of Healing,* which first appeared in 1905. The present volume is not an attempt to issue that popular book in a complete edition, but rather in abridged form. *The Ministry of Healing* is a book currently available from the publishers, and enjoys a large annual sale.

The insights and understanding of life, as reflected in the author's message, are as timely today as when they first appeared in print. The author's observations on such subjects as the use of alcohol and tobacco (pages 96-122), prenatal influence (pages 24-30), child guidance (pages 31-62), and many others, are in harmony with today's findings in science and education.

It is hoped that the reader will find in this book the key to open up the possibilities of a fresh and exuberant experience in life's best things.

PUBLISHERS AND TRUSTEES OF
ELLEN G. WHITE ESTATE.

Contents

Better Living 1
Life in the Home 6
Secrets of a Happy Marriage 11
Blueprint for a Modern Home 18
Cares of the Mother 24
Understanding the Child 31
Building Family Morale 39
Education Begins at Home 46
What Shall the Child Read? 54
Health Begins at Home 63
Feeding the Family 68
Choosing the Best Food 80
A Balanced Diet 86
Clothes for the Family 90
Stimulants and Narcotics 96
Liquor and Modern Life 105
Intemperance Can Be Cured 113

The Road to Health 123
Simple Remedies 127
Home Nursing 134
The Mental Outlook 137
Benefits of Outdoor Life 151
The Power of Prayer 156
A Servant of Humanity 164
Ministry to the Sick and Needy 173
With Nature and With God 188
Adventures in Faith 194
Healing the Soul 206
Call to Service 220
May We Know God? 227
The Quest for Truth 241
The Incomparable Book 248
Everyday Religion 255
Living With Others 268
The Highest Experience 279

Better Living

EDUCATION in health principles was never more needed than now. Many transgress the laws of health through ignorance, and they need instruction. But the greater number know better than they do. They need to be impressed with the importance of making their knowledge a guide of life.

Too little attention is generally given to the preservation of health. It is far better to prevent disease than to know how to treat it when contracted.

It is the duty of every person, for his own sake, and for the sake of humanity, to inform himself in regard to the laws of life, and conscientiously to obey them. All need to become acquainted with that most wonderful of all organisms, the human body. They should understand the functions of the various organs and the dependence of one upon another for the healthy action of all. They should study the influence of the mind upon the body, and of the body upon the mind, and the laws by which they are governed.

Disease is an effort of nature to free the system from conditions that result from a violation of the laws of health. In case of sickness, the cause should be ascertained. Unhealthful conditions should be changed, wrong habits corrected. Then nature is to be assisted in her effort to expel impu-

1

rities and to reestablish right conditions in the system.

Pure air, sunlight, abstemiousness, rest, exercise, proper diet, the use of water, trust in divine power—these are the true remedies. Every person should have a knowledge of nature's remedial agencies and how to apply them. It is essential both to understand the principles involved in the treatment of the sick and to have a practical training that will enable one rightly to use this knowledge.

The use of natural remedies requires an amount of care and effort that many are not willing to give. Nature's process of healing and upbuilding is gradual, and to the impatient it seems slow. The surrender of hurtful indulgences requires sacrifice. But in the end it will be found that nature, untrammeled, does her work wisely and well. Those who persevere in obedience to her laws will reap the reward in health of body and health of mind.

We cannot be too often reminded that health does not depend on chance. It is a result of obedience to law. This is recognized by the contestants in athletic games and trials of strength. These men make the most careful preparation. They submit to thorough training and strict discipline. Every physical habit is carefully regulated. They know that neglect, excess, or carelessness, which weakens or cripples any organ or function of the body, would ensure defeat.

Life Not a Mimic Battle

How much more important is such carefulness to ensure success in the conflict of life. It is not mimic battles in which we are engaged. We are waging a warfare upon which hang eternal results. Whatever injures the health not only lessens physical vigor, but tends to weaken the mental and moral powers. Indulgence in any unhealthful practice makes it more difficult for one to discriminate between right and wrong, and hence more difficult to resist evil. It increases the danger of failure and defeat.

"They which run in a race run all, but one receiveth the prize." 1 Corinthians 9:24. In the warfare in which we are engaged, all may win who will discipline themselves by obedience to right principles. The practice of these principles in the details of life is too often looked upon as unimportant —a matter too trivial to demand attention. But in view of the issues at stake, nothing with which we have to do is small. Every act casts its weight into the scale that determines life's victory or defeat. The Scripture bids us, "So run, that ye may obtain."

Pointing to the self-denial practiced by the contestants in the ancient Greek games, the apostle Paul writes: "Every man that striveth for the mastery is temperate in all things. Now they do it to obtain a corruptible crown; but we an incorruptible. I therefore so run, not as uncertainly; so fight I, not as one that beateth the air: but I keep under my body, and bring it into subjection: lest that by any means, when I have preached to others, I myself should be a castaway." Verses 25-27.

The foundation of all enduring reform is the law of God. We are to present in clear, distinct lines the need of obeying this law. Its principles must be kept before the people. They are as everlasting and inexorable as God Himself.

One of the most deplorable effects of the original apostasy was the loss of man's power of self-control. Only as this power is regained, can there be real progress.

The body is the only medium through which the mind

3

and the soul are developed for the upbuilding of character. Hence it is that the adversary of souls directs his temptations to the enfeebling and degrading of the physical powers. His success here means the surrender to evil of the whole being. The tendencies of our physical nature, unless under the dominion of a higher power, will surely work ruin and death.

The body is to be brought into subjection. The higher powers of the being are to rule. The passions are to be controlled by the will, which is itself to be under the control of God. The kingly power of reason, sanctified by divine grace, is to bear sway in our lives.

The requirements of God must be brought home to the conscience. Men and women must be awakened to the duty of self-mastery, the need of purity, freedom from every depraving appetite and defiling habit. They need to be impressed with the fact that all their powers of mind and body are the gift of God, and are to be preserved in the best possible condition for His service.

In that ancient ritual which was the gospel in symbol, no blemished offering could be brought to God's altar. The sacrifice that was to represent Christ must be spotless. The Word of God points to this as an illustration of what His children are to be—"holy and without blemish," "a living sacrifice," "well pleasing to God." Ephesians 5:27; Romans 12:1, R.V., margin.

Apart from divine power no genuine reform can be effected. Human barriers against natural and cultivated tendencies are but as the sandbank against the torrent. Not until the life of Christ becomes a vitalizing power in our lives can we resist the temptations that assail us from within and from without.

4

Christ came to this world and lived the law of God that man might have perfect mastery over the natural inclinations which corrupt the soul. The Physician of soul and body, He gives victory over warring lusts. He has provided every facility that man may possess completeness of character.

When one surrenders to Christ, the mind is brought under the control of the law; but it is the royal law, which proclaims liberty to every captive. By becoming one with Christ, man is made free. Subjection to the will of Christ means restoration to perfect manhood.

Obedience Brings Liberty

Obedience to God is liberty from the thralldom of sin, deliverance from human passion and impulse. Man may stand conqueror of himself, conqueror of his own inclinations, conqueror of principalities and powers, and of "the rulers of the darkness of this world," and of "spiritual wickedness in high places." Ephesians 6:12.

In no place is such instruction as this more needed, and nowhere will it be productive of greater good, than in the home. Parents have to do with the very foundation of habit and character. By their example and teaching, the destiny of their households is decided. The children will be what their parents make them.

If parents could be led to trace the result of their action, and could see how, by their example and teaching, they perpetuate and increase the power of sin or the power of righteousness, a change would certainly be made. Many would turn away from tradition and custom, and accept the divine principles of life.

5

Life in the Home

SOCIETY is composed of families, and is what the heads of families make it. Out of the heart "are the issues of life" (Proverbs 4:23); and the heart of the community, of the church, and of the nation is the household. The well-being of society, the success of the church, the prosperity of the nation, depend upon home influences.

The importance and the opportunities of the homelife are illustrated in the life of Jesus. He who came from heaven to be our example and teacher spent thirty years as a member of the household at Nazareth. Concerning these years the Bible record is very brief. No mighty miracles attracted the attention of the multitude. No eager throngs followed His steps or listened to His words. Yet during all these years He was fulfilling His divine mission. He lived as one of us, sharing the homelife, submitting to its discipline, performing its duties, bearing its burdens. In the sheltering care of a humble home, participating in the experiences of our common lot, He "increased in wisdom and stature, and in favor with God and man." Luke 2:52.

The Saviour's early years are more than an example to the youth. They are a lesson, and should be an encouragement, to every parent. The circle of family and neighborhood duties is the very first field of effort for those who would work for the uplifting of their fellowmen. There is no more important field of effort than that committed to the founders and guardians of the home. No work entrusted to human beings involves greater or more far-reaching results than does the work of fathers and mothers.

It is by the youth and children of today that the future of society is to be determined, and what these youth and children shall be depends upon the home. To the lack of right home training may be traced the larger share of the disease and misery and crime that curse humanity. If the home-life were pure and true, if the children who went forth from its care were prepared to meet life's responsibilities and dangers, what a change would be seen in the world!

Great efforts are put forth, time and money and labor almost without limit are expended, in enterprises and institutions for reforming the victims of evil habits. And even these efforts are inadequate to meet the great necessity. Yet how small is the result! How few are permanently reclaimed!

Multitudes long for a better life, but they lack courage and resolution to break away from the power of habit. They shrink from the effort and struggle and sacrifice demanded, and their lives are wrecked and ruined. Thus even men of the brightest minds, men of high aspirations and noble powers, otherwise fitted by nature and education to fill positions of trust and responsibility, are degraded and lost for this life and for the life to come.

For those who do reform, how bitter the struggle to regain their manhood! And all their life long, in a shattered constitution, a wavering will, impaired intellect, and weakened soul power, many reap the harvest of their evil sowing.

7

How much more might be accomplished if the evil were dealt with at the beginning!

This work rests, in a great degree, with parents. In the efforts put forth to stay the progress of intemperance and of other evils that are eating like a cancer in the social body, if more attention were given to teaching parents how to form the habits and character of their children, a hundred-fold more good would result. Habit, which is so terrible a force for evil, it is in their power to make a force for good. They have to do with the stream at its source, and it rests with them to direct it rightly.

Foundation for a Happy Life

Parents may lay for their children the foundation for a healthy, happy life. They may send them forth from their homes with moral stamina to resist temptation, and courage and strength to wrestle successfully with life's problems. They may inspire in them the purpose, and develop the power, to make their lives an honor to God and a blessing to the world. They may make straight paths for their feet, through sunshine and shadow, to the glorious heights above.

The mission of the home extends beyond its own members. The Christian home is to be an object lesson, illustrating the excellence of the true principles of life. Such an illustration will be a power for good in the world. Far more powerful than any sermon that can be preached is the influence of a true home upon human hearts and lives. As the youth go out from such a home, the lessons they have learned are imparted. Nobler principles of life are introduced into other households, and an uplifting influence works in the community.

8

There are many others to whom we might make our homes a blessing. Our social entertainments should not be governed by the dictates of worldly custom, but by the Spirit of Christ and the teaching of His Word.

"When thou makest a dinner or a supper," Christ says, "call not thy friends, nor thy brethren, neither thy kinsmen, nor thy rich neighbors; lest they also bid thee again, and a recompense be made thee. But when thou makest a feast, call the poor, the maimed, the lame, the blind: and thou shalt be blessed; for they cannot recompense thee: for thou shalt be recompensed at the resurrection of the just." Luke 14:12-14.

These are guests whom it will lay on you no great burden to receive. You will not need to provide for them elaborate or expensive entertainment. You will need to make no effort at display. The warmth of a genial welcome, a place at your fireside, a seat at your home table, the privilege of sharing the blessing of the hour of prayer, would to many of these be like a glimpse of heaven.

Our sympathies are to overflow the boundaries of self and the enclosure of family walls. There are precious opportunities for those who will make their homes a blessing to others. Social influence is a wonderful power. We can use it, if we will, as a means of helping those about us.

A Hand Stretched Out

Our homes should be a place of refuge for the tempted youth. Many there are who stand at the parting of the ways. Every influence, every impression, is determining the choice that shapes their destiny both here and hereafter. Evil invites them. Its resorts are made bright and attractive.

They have a welcome for every comer. All about us are youth who have no home, and many whose homes have no helpful, uplifting power; and the youth drift into evil. They are going down to ruin within the very shadow of our own doors.

These youth need a hand stretched out to them in sympathy. Kind words simply spoken, little attentions simply bestowed, will sweep away the clouds of temptation which gather over the soul. The true expression of heaven-born sympathy has power to open the door of hearts that need the fragrance of Christlike words, and the simple, delicate touch of the spirit of Christ's love. If we would show an interest in the youth, invite them to our homes, and surround them with cheering, helpful influences, there are many who would gladly turn their steps into the upward path.

Our time here is short. We can pass through this world but once; as we pass along, let us make the most of life. If we will open our hearts and homes to the divine principles of life, we shall become channels for currents of life-giving power. From our homes will flow streams of healing, bringing life, and beauty, and fruitfulness where now are barrenness and dearth.

Secrets of a Happy Marriage

HE WHO gave Eve to Adam as a helpmeet, performed His first miracle at a marriage festival. In the festal hall where friends and kindred rejoiced together, Christ began His public ministry. Thus He sanctioned marriage, recognizing it as an institution that He Himself had established. He ordained that men and women should be united in holy wedlock, to rear families whose members, crowned with honor, should be recognized as members of the family above.

Christ honored the marriage relation by making it also a symbol of the union between Him and His redeemed ones. He Himself is the Bridegroom; the bride is the church, of which, as His chosen one, He says, "Thou art all fair, My love; there is no spot in thee." Song of Solomon 4:7.

Christ "loved the church, and gave Himself for it; that He might sanctify and cleanse it; . . . that it should be holy and without blemish. So ought men to love their wives." Ephesians 5:25-28.

The family tie is the closest, the most tender and sacred, of any on earth. It was designed to be a blessing to mankind. And it is a blessing wherever the marriage covenant is entered into intelligently, in the fear of God, and with due consideration for its responsibilities.

11

Those who are contemplating marriage should consider what will be the character and influence of the home they are founding. As they become parents, a sacred trust is committed to them. Upon them depends in a great measure the well-being of their children in this world and their happiness in the world to come. To a great extent they determine both the physical and the moral stamp that the little ones receive. And upon the character of the home depends the condition of society; the weight of each family's influence will tell in the upward or the downward scale.

Choosing a Life Companion

The choice of a life companion should be such as best to secure physical, mental, and spiritual well-being for parents and for their children—such as will enable both parents and children to bless their fellowmen and to honor their Creator.

Before assuming the responsibilities involved in marriage, young men and young women should have such an experience in practical life as will prepare them for its duties and its burdens. Early marriages are not to be encouraged. A relation so important as marriage and so far-reaching in its results should not be entered upon hastily, without sufficient preparation, and before the mental and physical powers are well developed.

The parties may not have worldy wealth, but they should have the far greater blessing of health. And in most cases there should not be a great disparity in age. A neglect of this rule may result in seriously impairing the health of the younger. And often the children are robbed of physical and mental strength. They cannot receive from an aged parent

12

the care and companionship which their young lives demand, and they may be deprived by death of the father or the mother at the very time when love and guidance are most needed.

Religion and Marriage

It is only in Christ that a marriage alliance can be safely formed. Human love should draw its closest bonds from divine love. Only where Christ reigns can there be deep, true, unselfish affection.

Love is a precious gift, which we receive from Jesus. Pure and holy affection is not a feeling, but a principle. Those who are actuated by true love are neither unreasonable nor blind. Taught by the Holy Spirit, they love God supremely, and their neighbor as themselves.

Let those who are contemplating marriage weigh every sentiment and watch every development of character in the one with whom they think to unite their life destiny. Let every step toward a marriage alliance be characterized by modesty, simplicity, sincerity, and an earnest purpose to please and honor God. Marriage affects the afterlife both in this world and in the world to come. A sincere Christian will make no plans that God cannot approve.

If you are blessed with God-fearing parents, seek counsel of them. Open to them your hopes and plans, learn the lessons which their life experiences have taught, and you will be saved many a heartache. Above all, make Christ your counselor. Study His Word with prayer.

Under such guidance let a young woman accept as a life companion only one who possesses pure, manly traits of character, one who is diligent, aspiring, and honest, one who loves and fears God. Let a young man seek one to stand by his side who is fitted to bear her share of life's burdens, one whose influence will ennoble and refine him, and who will make him happy in her love.

"A prudent wife is from the Lord." "The heart of her husband doth safely trust in her. . . . She will do him good and not evil all the days of her life." "She openeth her mouth with wisdom; and in her tongue is the law of kindness. She looketh well to the ways of her household, and eateth not the bread of idleness. Her childern arise up and, call her blessed; her husband also, and he praiseth her," saying, "Many daughters have done virtuously, but thou excellest them all." He who gains such a wife "findeth a good thing, and obtaineth favor of the Lord." Proverbs 19:14; 31:11, 12, 26-29; 18:22.

The Union of Two Lives

However carefully and wisely marriage may have been entered into, few couples are completely united when the marriage ceremony is performed. The real union of the two in wedlock is the work of the afteryears.

As life with its burden of perplexity and care meets the newly wedded pair, the romance with which imagination so often invests marriage disappears. Husband and wife learn each other's character as it was impossible to learn it in their previous association. This is a most critical period in their experience. The happiness and usefulness of their whole future life depend upon their taking a right course now. Often they discern in each other unsuspected weaknesses and defects; but the hearts that love has united will discern excellencies also heretofore unknown. Let all seek

14

to discover the excellencies rather than the defects. Often it is our own attitude, the atmosphere that surrounds ourselves, which determines what will be revealed to us in another.

There are many who regard the expression of love as a weakness, and they maintain a reserve that repels others. This spirit checks the current of sympathy. As the social and generous impulses are repressed, they wither, and the heart becomes desolate and cold. We should beware of this error. Love cannot long exist without expression. Let not the heart of one connected with you starve for the want of kindness and sympathy.

A Foretaste of Heaven

Though difficulties, perplexities, and discouragements may arise, let neither husband nor wife harbor the thought that their union is a mistake or a disappointment. Determine to be all that it is possible to be to each other. Continue the early attentions. In every way encourage each other in fighting the battles of life. Study to advance the happiness of each other. Let there be mutual love, mutual forbearance. Then marriage, instead of being the end of love, will be as it were the very beginning of love. The warmth of true friendship, the love that binds heart to heart, is a foretaste of the joys of heaven.

Around every family there is a sacred circle that should be kept unbroken. Within this circle no other person has a right to come: Let not the husband or the wife permit another to share the confidences that belong solely to themselves.

Let each give love rather than exact it. Cultivate that

15

which is noblest in yourselves, and be quick to recognize the good qualities in each other. The consciousness of being appreciated is a wonderful stimulus and satisfaction. Sympathy and respect encourage the striving after excellence, and love itself increases as it stimulates to nobler aims.

Neither the husband nor the wife should merge his or her individuality in that of the other. Each has a personal relation to God. Of Him each is to ask: "What is right?" "What is wrong?" "How may I best fulfill life's purpose?" Let the wealth of your affection flow forth to Him who gave His life for you. Make Christ first and last and best in everything. As your love for Him becomes deeper and stronger, your love for each other will be purified and strengthened.

The spirit that Christ manifests toward us is the spirit that husband and wife are to manifest toward each other. "As Christ also hath loved us," "walk in love." "As the church is subject unto Christ, so let the wives be to their own husbands in everything. Husbands, love your wives, even as Christ also loved the church, and gave Himself for it." Ephesians 5:2, 24, 25.

Neither the husband nor the wife should attempt to exercise over the other an arbitrary control. Do not try to compel each other to yield to your wishes. You cannot do this and retain each other's love. Be kind, patient, and forbearing, considerate, and courteous. By the grace of God you can succeed in making each other happy, as in your marriage vow you promised to do.

But remember that happiness will not be found in shutting yourselves up to yourselves, satisfied to pour out all your affection upon each other. Seize upon every opportunity for contributing to the happiness of those around you. Remember that true joy can be found only in unselfish service.

Forbearance and unselfishness mark the words and acts of all who live the new life in Christ. As you seek to live His life, striving to conquer self and selfishness and to minister to the needs of others, you will gain victory after victory. Thus your influence will bless the world.

Take Christ as Helper

Men and women can reach God's ideal for them if they will take Christ as their helper. What human wisdom cannot do, His grace will accomplish for those who give themselves to Him in loving trust. His providence can unite hearts in bonds that are of heavenly origin. Love will not be a mere exchange of soft and flattering words. The loom of heaven weaves with warp and woof finer, yet more firm, than can be woven by the looms of earth. The result is not a tissue fabric, but a texture that will bear wear and test and trial. Heart will be bound to heart in the golden bonds of a love that is enduring.

17

Blueprint for a Modern Home

THE gospel is a wonderful simplifier of life's problems. Its instruction, heeded, would make plain many a perplexity, and save us from many an error. It teaches us to estimate things at their true value, and to give the most effort to the things of greatest worth—the things that will endure. This lesson is needed by those upon whom rests the responsibility of selecting a home. They should not allow themselves to be diverted from the highest aim. Let them remember that the home on earth is to be a symbol of, and a preparation for, the home in heaven. Life is a training school, from which parents and children are to be graduated to the higher school in the mansions of God. As the location for a home is sought, let this purpose direct the choice. Be not controlled by the desire for wealth, the dictates of fashion, or the customs of society. Consider what will tend most to simplicity, purity, health, and real worth.

The world over, cities are becoming hotbeds of vice. On every hand are the sights and sounds of evil. Everywhere are enticements to sensuality and dissipation. The tide of corruption and crime is continually swelling. Every day brings the record of violence—robberies, murders, suicides, and crimes unnamable.

Artificial City Life

Life in the cities is false and artificial. The intense passion for money getting, the whirl of excitement and pleasure seeking, the thirst for display, the luxury and extravagance, all are forces that, with the great masses of mankind, are turning the mind from life's true purpose. They are opening the door to a thousand evils. Upon the youth they have almost irresistible power.

One of the most subtle and dangerous temptations that assail the children and youth in the cities is the love of pleasure. Holidays are numerous; games and horse racing draw thousands, and the whirl of excitement and pleasure attracts them away from the sober duties of life. Money that should have been saved for better uses is frittered away for amusements.

Through the working of trusts, and the results of labor unions and strikes, the conditions of life in the city are constantly becoming more and more difficult. Serious troubles are before us; and for many families removal from the cities will become a necessity.

The physical surroundings in the cities are often a peril to health. The constant liability to contact with disease, the prevalence of foul air, impure water, impure food, the crowded, dark, unhealthful dwellings, are some of the many evils to be met.

A Garden Home in Eden

It was not God's purpose that people should be crowded into cities, huddled together in terraces and tenements. In the beginning He placed our first parents amidst the beau-

19

tiful sights and sounds He desires us to rejoice in today. The more nearly we come into harmony with God's original plan, the more favorable will be our position to secure health of body and mind and soul.

An expensive dwelling, elaborate furnishings, display, luxury, and ease, do not furnish the conditions essential to a happy, useful life. Jesus came to this earth to accomplish the greatest work ever accomplished among men. He came as God's ambassador, to show us how to live so as to secure life's best results. What were the conditions chosen by the infinite Father for His Son? A secluded home in the Galilean hills; a household sustained by honest, self-respecting labor; a life of simplicity; daily conflict with difficulty and hardship; self-sacrifice, economy, and patient, gladsome service; the hour of study at His mother's side, with the open scroll of Scripture; the quiet of dawn or twilight in the green valley; the holy ministries of nature; the study of creation and providence; and the soul's communion with God—these were the conditions and opportunities of the early life of Jesus.

So with the great majority of the best and noblest men of all ages. Read the history of Abraham, Jacob, and Joseph, of Moses, David, and Elisha. Study the lives of men of later times who have most worthily filled positions of trust and responsibility, the men whose influence has been most effective for the world's uplifting.

How many of these were reared in country homes. They knew little of luxury. They did not spend their youth in amusement. Many were forced to struggle with poverty and hardship. They early learned to work, and their active life in the open air gave vigor and elasticity to all their faculties. Forced to depend upon their own resources, they learned to combat difficulties and to surmount obstacles, and they gained courage and perseverance. They learned the lessons of self-reliance and self-control. Sheltered in a great degree from evil associations, they were satisfied with natural pleasures and wholesome companionships. They were simple in their tastes and temperate in their habits. They were governed by principle, and they grew up pure and strong and true. When called to their lifework, they brought to it physical and mental power, buoyancy of spirit, ability to plan and execute, and steadfastness in resisting evil, that made them a positive power for good in the world.

Life's Best Things

Better than any other inheritance of wealth you can give to your children will be the gift of a healthy body, a sound mind, and a noble character. Those who understand what constitutes life's true success will be wise betimes. They will keep in view life's best things in their choice of a home.

Instead of dwelling where only the works of men can be seen, where the sights and sounds frequently suggest thoughts of evil, where turmoil and confusion bring weariness and disquietude, go where you can look upon the works of God. Find rest of spirit in the beauty and quietude and peace of nature. Let the eye rest on the green fields, the groves, and the hills. Look up to the blue sky, unobscured by the city's dust and smoke, and breathe the invigorating air of heaven. Go where, apart from the distractions and dissipations of city life, you can give your children your companionship, where you can teach them to learn of God

21

through His works, and train them for lives of integrity and usefulness.

Our artificial habits deprive us of many blessings and much enjoyment, and unfit us for living the most useful lives. Elaborate and expensive furnishings are a waste not only of money, but of that which is a thousandfold more precious. They bring into the home a heavy burden of care and labor and perplexity.

In many a home the wife and mother has no time to read, to keep herself well informed, no time to be a companion to her husband, no time to keep in touch with the developing minds of her children. There is no time or place for the precious Saviour to be a close, dear companion. Little by little she sinks into a mere household drudge, her strength and time and interest absorbed in the things that perish with the using. Too late she awakes to find herself almost a stranger in her own home. The precious opportunities once hers to influence her dear ones for the higher life, unimproved, have passed away forever.

Live on a Wiser Plan

Let the homemakers resolve to live on a wiser plan. Let it be your first aim to make a pleasant home. Be sure to provide the facilities that will lighten labor and promote health and comfort. Plan for the entertainment of the guests whom Christ has bidden us welcome, and of whom He says, "Inasmuch as ye have done it unto one of the least of these My brethren, ye have done it unto Me." Matthew 25:40.

Furnish your home with things plain and simple, things that will bear handling, that can be easily kept clean, and

22

that can be replaced without great expense. By exercising taste, you can make a very simple home attractive and inviting, if love and contentment are there.

God loves the beautiful. He has clothed the earth and the heavens with beauty, and with a Father's joy He watches the delight of His children in the things that He has made. He desires us to surround our homes with the beauty of natural things.

Nearly all dwellers in the country, however poor, could have about their homes a bit of grassy lawn, a few shade trees, flowering shrubbery, or fragrant blossoms. And far more than any artificial adorning will they minister to the happiness of the household. They will bring into the home-life a softening, refining influence, strengthening the love of nature, and drawing the members of the household nearer to one another and nearer to God.

Cares of the Mother

WHAT the parents are, that, to a great extent, the children will be. The physical conditions of the parents, their dispositions and appetites, their mental and moral tendencies, are, to a greater or lesser degree, reproduced in their children.

The nobler the aims, the higher the mental and spiritual endowments, and the better developed the physical powers of the parents, the better will be the life equipment they give their children. In cultivating that which is best in themselves, parents are exerting an influence to mold society and to uplift future generations.

Fathers and mothers need to understand their responsibility. The world is full of snares for the feet of the young. Multitudes are attracted by a life of selfish and sensual pleasure. They cannot discern the hidden dangers or the fearful ending of the path that seems to them the way of happiness. Through the indulgence of appetite and passion, their energies are wasted, and millions are ruined for this world and for the world to come. Parents should remember that their children must encounter these temptations. Even before the birth of the child, the preparation should begin that will enable it to fight successfully the battle against evil.

Especially does responsibility rest upon the mother. She, by whose lifeblood the child is nourished and its physical frame built up, imparts to it also mental and spiritual influences that tend to the shaping of mind and character. It was Jochebed, the Hebrew mother, who, strong in faith, was "not afraid of the king's commandment," of whom was born Moses, the deliverer of Israel. Hebrews 11:23. It was Hannah, the woman of prayer and self-sacrifice and heavenly inspiration, who gave birth to Samuel, the heaven-instructed child, the incorruptible judge, the founder of Israel's sacred schools. It was Elisabeth, the kinswoman and kindred spirit of Mary of Nazareth, who was the mother of the Saviour's herald.

The carefulness with which the mother should guard her habits of life is taught in the Scriptures. When the Lord would raise up Samson as a deliverer for Israel, "the angel of Jehovah" appeared to the mother, with special instruction concerning her habits and also for the treatment of her child. "Beware," he said, "and drink no wine nor strong drink, and eat not any unclean thing." Judges 13:13, 4, R.V.

The effect of prenatal influences is by many parents looked upon as a matter of little moment; but heaven does not so regard it. The message sent by an angel of God, and twice given in the most solemn manner, shows it to be deserving of our most careful thought.

Living by Principle

In the words spoken to the Hebrew mother, God speaks to all mothers in every age. "Let her beware," the angel said; "all that I commanded her let her observe." The well-being of the child will be affected by the habits of the mother.

25

Her appetites and passions are to be controlled by principle. There is something for her to shun, something for her to work against, if she fulfills God's purpose for her in giving her a child. If before the birth of her child she is self-indulgent, if she is selfish, impatient, and exacting, these traits will be reflected in the disposition of the child. Thus many children have received as a birthright almost unconquerable tendencies to evil.

But if the mother unswervingly adheres to right principles, if she is temperate and self-denying, if she is kind, gentle, and unselfish, she may give her child these same precious traits of character. Very explicit was the command prohibiting the use of wine by the mother. Every drop of strong drink taken by her to gratify appetite endangers the physical, mental, and moral health of her child, and is a direct sin against her Creator.

Many advisers urge that every wish of the mother should be gratified; that if she desires any article of food, however harmful, she should freely indulge her appetite. Such advice is false and mischievous. The mother's physical needs should in no case be neglected. Two lives are depending upon her, and her wishes should be tenderly regarded, her needs generously supplied. But at this time above all others she should avoid, in diet and in every other line, whatever would lessen physical or mental strength. By the command of God Himself she is placed under the most solemn obligation to exercise self-control.

How the Husband Can Help

The strength of the mother should be tenderly cherished. Instead of spending her precious strength in exhausting

26

labor, her care and burdens should be lessened. Often the husband and father is unacquainted with the physical laws which the well-being of his family requires him to understand. Absorbed in the struggle for a livelihood, or bent on acquiring wealth, and pressed with cares and perplexities, he allows to rest upon the wife and mother burdens that overtax her strength at the most critical period, and cause feebleness and disease.

Many a husband and father might learn a helpful lesson from the carefulness of the faithful shepherd. Jacob, when urged to undertake a rapid and difficult journey, made answer:

"The children are tender, and the flocks and herds with young are with me: and if men should overdrive them one day, all the flock will die." "I will lead on softly, according as the cattle that goeth before me and the children be able to endure." Genesis 33:13, 14.

In life's toilsome way let the husband and father "lead on softly," as the companion of his journey is able to endure. Amidst the world's eager rush for wealth and power, let him learn to stay his steps, to comfort and support the one who is called to walk by his side.

Cultivate a Happy Disposition

The mother should cultivate a cheerful, contented, happy disposition. Every effort in this direction will be abundantly repaid in both the physical well-being and the moral character of her children. A cheerful spirit will promote the happiness of her family, and in a very great degree improve her own health.

Let the husband aid his wife by his sympathy and unfail-

27

ing affection. If he wishes to keep her fresh and gladsome, so that she will be as sunshine in the home, let him help her bear her burdens. His kindness and loving courtesy will be to her a precious encouragement, and the happiness he imparts will bring joy and peace to his own heart.

The husband and father who is morose, selfish, and overbearing is not only unhappy himself, but he casts gloom upon all the inmates of his home. He will reap the result in seeing his wife dispirited and sickly, and his children marred with his own unlovely temper.

If the mother is deprived of the care and comforts she should have, if she is allowed to exhaust her strength through overwork or through anxiety and gloom, her children will be robbed of the vital force and of the mental elasticity and cheerful buoyancy they should inherit. Far better will it be to make the mother's life bright and cheerful, to shield her from want, wearing labor, and depressing care, and let the children inherit good constitutions, so that they may battle their way through life with their own energetic strength.

Great is the honor and the responsibility placed upon fathers and mothers, in that they are to stand in the place of God to their children. Their character, their daily life, their methods of training, will interpret His words to the little ones. Their influence will win or repel the child's confidence in the Lord's assurances.

Happy are the parents whose lives are a true reflection of the divine, so that the promises and commands of God awaken in the child gratitude and reverence; the parents whose tenderness and justice and long-suffering interpret to the child the love and justice and long-suffering of God; and who, by teaching the child to love and trust and obey them, are teaching him to love and trust and obey his Father in heaven. Parents who impart to a child such a gift have endowed him with a treasure more precious than the wealth of all the ages—a treasure as enduring as eternity.

In the children committed to her care, every mother has a sacred charge from God. "Take this son, this daughter," He says; "train it for Me; give it a character polished after the similitude of a palace, that it may shine in the courts of the Lord forever."

Written in the Book of Life

The mother's work often seems to her an unimportant service. It is a work that is rarely appreciated. Others know little of her many cares and burdens. Her days are occupied with a round of little duties, all calling for patient effort, for self-control, for tact, wisdom, and self-sacrificing love; yet she cannot boast of what she has done as any great achievement. She has only kept things in the home running smoothly; often weary and perplexed, she has tried to speak kindly to the children, to keep them busy and happy, and to guide the little feet in the right path. She feels that she has accomplished nothing. But it is not so. Heavenly angels watch the careworn mother, noting the burdens she carries day by day. Her name may not have been heard in the world, but it is written in the Lamb's book of life.

There is a God above, and the light and glory from His throne rests upon the faithful mother as she tries to educate her children to resist the influence of evil. No other work can equal hers in importance. She has not, like the artist, to paint a form of beauty upon canvas, nor, like the sculptor, to chisel it from marble. She has not, like the author, to embody a noble thought in words of power, nor, like the musician, to express a beautiful sentiment in melody. It is hers, with the help of God, to develop in a human soul the likeness of the divine.

The mother who appreciates this will regard her opportunities as priceless. Earnestly will she seek, in her own character and by her methods of training, to present before her children the highest ideal. Earnestly, patiently, courageously, she will endeavor to improve her own abilities, that she may use aright the highest powers of the mind in the training of her children. Earnestly will she inquire at every step, "What hath God spoken?" Diligently she will study His Word. She will keep her eyes fixed upon Christ, that her own daily experience in the lowly round of care and duty may be a true reflection of the one true Life.

Understanding the Child

NOT only the habits of the mother, but the training of the child were included in the angel's instruction to the Hebrew parents. It was not enough that Samson, the child who was to deliver Israel, should have a good legacy at his birth. This was to be followed by careful training. From infancy he was to be trained to habits of strict temperance.

Similar instruction was given in regard to John the Baptist. Before the birth of the child, the message sent from heaven to the father was:

"Thou shalt have joy and gladness; and many shall rejoice at his birth. For he shall be great in the sight of the Lord, and he shall drink no wine nor strong drink; and he shall be filled with the Holy Spirit." Luke 1:14, 15, A.R.V.

On heaven's record of noble men the Saviour declared that there stood not one greater than John the Baptist. The work committed to him was one demanding not only physical energy and endurance, but the highest qualities of mind and soul. So important was right physical training as a preparation for this work that the highest angel in heaven was sent with a message of instruction to the parents of the child.

The directions given concerning the Hebrew children teach us that nothing which affects the child's physical well-being is to be neglected. Nothing is unimportant. Every influence that affects the health of the body has its bearing upon mind and character.

Importance of Early Training

Too much importance cannot be placed upon the early training of children. The lessons learned, the habits formed, during the years of infancy and childhood, have more to do with the formation of the character and the direction of the life than have all the instruction and training of afteryears.

Parents need to consider this. They should understand the principles that underlie the care and training of children. They should be capable of rearing them in physical, mental, and moral health. Parents should study the laws of nature. They should become acquainted with the organism of the human body. They need to understand the functions of the various organs, and their relation and dependence. They should study the relation of the mental to the physical powers, and the conditions required for the healthy action of each. To assume the responsibilities of parenthood without such preparation is a sin.

Most of the evils that are bringing misery and ruin to the race might be prevented, and the power to deal with them rests to a great degree with parents. It is not a "mysterious providence" that removes the little children. God does not desire their death. He gives them to the parents to be trained for usefulness here, and for heaven hereafter.

The more quiet and simple the life of the child, the more favorable it will be to both physical and mental development. At all times the mother should endeavor to be quiet, calm, and self-possessed. Many infants are extremely susceptible to nervous excitement, and the mother's gentle, unhurried manner will have a soothing influence that will be of untold benefit to the child.

Babies require warmth, but a serious error is often committed in keeping them in overheated rooms, deprived to a great degree of fresh air. The practice of covering the infant's face while sleeping is harmful, since it prevents free respiration.

The baby should be kept free from every influence that would tend to weaken or to poison the system. The most scrupulous care should be taken to have everything about it sweet and clean. While it may be necessary to protect the little ones from sudden or too great changes of temperature, care should be taken, that, sleeping or waking, day or night, they breathe a pure, invigorating atmosphere.

In the preparation of the baby's wardrobe, convenience, comfort, and health should be sought before fashion or a desire to excite admiration.

Dressing the Child

If the dress of the child combines warmth, protection, and comfort, one of the chief causes of irritation and restlessness will be removed. The little one will have better health, and the mother will not find the care of the child so heavy a tax upon her strength and time.

Tight bands or waists hinder the action of the heart and lungs, and should be avoided. No part of the body should at any time be made uncomfortable by clothing that compresses any organ or restricts its freedom of movement. The clothing of all children should be loose enough to admit of the freest and fullest respiration, and so arranged that the shoulders will support its weight.

33

In some countries the custom of leaving bare the shoulders and limbs of little children still prevails. This custom cannot be too severely condemned. The limbs, being remote from the center of circulation, demand greater protection than the other parts of the body. The arteries that convey the blood to the extremities are large, providing for a sufficient quantity of blood to afford warmth and nutrition. But when the limbs are left unprotected or are insufficiently clad, the arteries and veins become contracted, the sensitive portions of the body are chilled, and the circulation of the blood hindered.

In growing children all the forces of nature need every advantage to enable them to perfect the physical frame. If the limbs are insufficiently protected, children, and especially girls, cannot be out of doors unless the weather is mild. So they are kept in, for fear of the cold. If children are well clothed, it will benefit them to exercise freely in the open air, summer or winter.

Mothers who desire their boys and girls to possess the vigor of health, should dress them properly, and encourage them in all reasonable weather to be much in the open air. It may require effort to break away from the chains of custom, and dress and educate the children with reference to health; but the result will amply repay the effort.

The Best Food for Infants

The best food for the infant is the food that nature provides. Of this it should not be needlessly deprived. It is a heartless thing for a mother, for the sake of convenience or social enjoyment, to seek to free herself from the tender office of nursing her little one.

The importance of training children to right dietetic habits can hardly be overestimated. The little ones need to learn that they eat to live, not live to eat. The training should begin with the infant in its mother's arms. The child should be given food only at regular intervals, and less frequently as it grows older. It should not be given sweets, or the food of older persons, which it is unable to digest. Care and regularity in the feeding of infants will not only promote health, and thus tend to make them quiet and sweet-tempered, but will lay the foundation of habits that will be a blessing to them in afteryears.

As children emerge from babyhood, great care should still be taken in educating their tastes and appetite. Often they are permitted to eat what they choose and when they choose, without reference to health. The pains and money so often lavished upon unwholesome dainties lead the young to think that the highest object in life, and that which yields the greatest amount of happiness, is to be able to indulge the appetite. The result of this training is gluttony, then comes sickness, which is usually followed by dosing with poisonous drugs.

Training the Appetite

Parents should train the appetites of their children, and should not permit the use of unwholesome foods. But in the effort to regulate the diet, we should be careful not to err in requiring children to eat that which is distasteful, or to eat more than is needed. Children have rights, they have preferences, and when these preferences are reasonable, they should be respected.

Regularity in eating should be carefully observed. Nothing should be eaten between meals, no confectionery, nuts, fruits, or food of any kind. Irregularities in eating destroy the healthful tone of the digestive organs, to the detriment of health and cheerfulness. And when the children come to the table, they do not relish wholesome food; their appetites crave that which is hurtful for them.

Mothers who gratify the desires of their children at the expense of health and happy tempers are sowing seeds of evil that will spring up and bear fruit. Self-indulgence grows with the growth of the little ones, and both mental and physical vigor are sacrificed. Mothers who do this work reap with bitterness the seed they have sown. They see their children grow up unfitted in mind and character to act a noble and useful part in society or in the home. The spiritual as well as the mental and physical powers suffer under the influence of unhealthful food. The conscience becomes stupefied, and the susceptibility to good impressions is impaired.

While the children should be taught to control the appetite and to eat with reference to health, let it be made plain that they are denying themselves only that which would do them harm. They give up hurtful things for something better. Let the table be made inviting and attractive, as it is supplied with the good things which God has so bountifully bestowed. Let mealtime be a cheerful, happy time. As we enjoy the gifts of God, let us respond by grateful praise to the Giver.

In many cases the sickness of children can be traced to errors in management. Irregularities in eating, insufficient clothing in the chilly evening, lack of vigorous exercise to keep the blood in healthy circulation, or lack of abundance of air for its purification may be the cause of the trouble. Let the parents study to find the causes of the sickness, and then remedy the wrong conditions as soon as possible.

All parents have it in their power to learn much concerning the care and prevention, and even the treatment, of disease. Especially ought the mother to know what to do in common cases of illness in her family. She should know how to minister to her sick child. Her love and insight should fit her to perform services for it which could not so well be trusted to a stranger's hand.

Simple Lessons in Physiology

Parents should early seek to interest their children in the study of physiology, and should teach them its simpler principles. Teach them how best to preserve the physical, mental, and spiritual powers, and how to use their gifts so that their lives may bring blessing to one another and honor to God. This knowledge is invaluable to the young. An education in the things that concern life and health is more important to them than a knowledge of many of the sciences taught in the schools.

Parents should live more for their children, and less for society. Study health subjects, and put your knowledge to a practical use. Teach your children to reason from cause to effect. Teach them that if they desire health and happiness they must obey the laws of nature. Though you may not see so rapid improvement as you desire, be not discouraged, but patiently and perseveringly continue your work.

Teach your children from the cradle to practice self-denial and self-control. Teach them to enjoy the beauties of nature, and in useful employments to exercise systematically all the powers of body and mind. Bring them up to have sound constitutions and good morals, to have sunny dispositions and sweet tempers. Impress upon their tender minds the truth that God does not design that we should live for present gratification merely, but for our ultimate good. Teach them that to yield to temptation is weak and wicked; to resist, noble and manly. These lessons will be as seed sown in good soil, and they will bear fruit that will make your hearts glad.

Sunshine in the Home

Above all things else, let parents surround their children with an atmosphere of cheerfulness, courtesy, and love. A home where love dwells, and where it is expressed in looks, in words, and in acts, is a place where angels delight to manifest their presence.

Parents, let the sunshine of love, cheerfulness, and happy contentment enter your own hearts, and let its sweet, cheering influence pervade your home. Manifest a kindly, forbearing spirit; and encourage the same in your children, cultivating all the graces that will brighten the homelife. The atmosphere thus created will be to the children what air and sunshine are to the vegetable world, promoting health and vigor of mind and body.

Building Family Morale

THE home should be to the children the most attractive place in the world, and the mother's presence should be its greatest attraction. Children have sensitive, loving natures. They are easily pleased, and easily made unhappy. By gentle discipline, in loving words and acts, mothers may bind their children to their hearts.

Young children love companionship, and can seldom enjoy themselves alone. They yearn for sympathy and tenderness. That which they enjoy, they think will please mother also; and it is natural for them to go to her with their little joys and sorrows. The mother should not wound their sensitive hearts by treating with indifference matters that, though trifling to her, are of great importance to them. Her sympathy and approval are precious. An approving glance, a word of encouragement or commendation, will be like sunshine in their hearts, often making the whole day happy.

Instead of sending her children from her, that she may not be annoyed by their noise or troubled by their little wants, let the mother plan amusement or light work to employ the active hands and minds.

By entering into their feelings, and directing their amusements and employments, the mother will gain the confidence of her children, and she can the more effectually correct

39

wrong habits or check the manifestations of selfishness or passion. A word of caution or reproof spoken at the right time will be of great value. By patient, watchful love she can turn the minds of the children in the right direction, cultivating in them beautiful and attractive traits of character.

Contentment With Simple Pleasures

Mothers should guard against training their children to be dependent and self-absorbed. Never lead them to think that they are the center, and that everything must revolve around them. Some parents give much time and attention to amusing their children, but children should be trained to amuse themselves, to exercise their own ingenuity and skill. Thus they will learn to be content with very simple pleasures. They should be taught to bear bravely their little disappointments and trials. Instead of calling attention to every trifling pain or hurt, divert their minds, teach them to pass lightly over little annoyances or discomforts. Study to suggest ways by which the children may learn to be thoughtful for others.

But let not the children be neglected. Burdened with many cares, mothers sometimes feel that they cannot take time patiently to instruct their little ones and give them love and sympathy. But they should remember that if the children do not find in their parents and in their home that which will satisfy their desire for sympathy and companionship, they will look to other sources, where both mind and character may be endangered.

For lack of time and thought, many a mother refuses her children some innocent pleasure, while busy fingers and weary eyes are diligently engaged on work designed only for adornment, something that, at best, will serve only to encourage vanity and extravagance in their young hearts. As the children approach manhood and womanhood, these lessons bear fruit in pride and moral worthlessness. The mother grieves over her children's faults, but does not realize that the harvest she is reaping is from seed which she herself planted.

Some mothers are not uniform in the treatment of their children. At times they indulge them to their injury; and again they refuse some innocent gratification that would make the childish heart very happy. In this they do not imitate Christ; He loved the children; He comprehended their feelings, and sympathized with them in their pleasures and their trials.

The husband and father is the head of the household. The wife looks to him for love and sympathy, and for aid in the training of the children, and this is right. The children are his as well as hers, and he is equally interested in their welfare. The children look to the father for support and guidance; he needs to have a right conception of life and of the influences and associations that should surround his family; above all, he should be controlled by the love and fear of God and by the teaching of His Word, that he may guide the feet of his children in the right way.

Lawmaker of the Home

The father is the lawmaker of the household; and, like Abraham, he should make the law of God the rule of his home. God said of Abraham, "I know him, that he will command his children and his household." Genesis 18:19. There would be no sinful neglect to restrain evil, no weak, unwise, indulgent favoritism; no yielding of his conviction of duty to the claims of mistaken affection. Abraham would not only give right instruction, but he would maintain the authority of just and righteous laws. God has given rules for our guidance. Children should not be left to wander away from the safe path marked out in God's Word into ways leading to danger, which are open on every side. Kindly, but firmly, with persevering, prayerful effort, their wrong desires should be restrained, their inclinations denied.

The father should enforce in his family the sterner virtues—energy, integrity, honesty, patience, courage, diligence, and practical usefulness. And what he requires of his children he himself should practice, illustrating these virtues in his own manly bearing.

But, fathers, do not discourage your children. Combine affection with authority, kindness and sympathy with firm restraint. Give some of your leisure hours to your children; become acquainted with them; associate with them in their work and in their sports, and win their confidence. Cultivate friendship with them, especially with your sons. In this way you will be a strong influence for good.

The father should do his part toward making home happy. Whatever his cares and business perplexities, they should not be permitted to overshadow his family; he should enter his home with smiles and pleasant words.

Worship Time With the Family

In a sense the father is the priest of the household, laying upon the family altar the morning and evening sacrifice. But the wife and children should unite in prayer, and join in the song of praise. In the morning before he leaves home for his daily labor, let the father gather his children about him and, bowing before God, commit them to the care of the Father in heaven. When the cares of the day are past, let the family unite in offering grateful prayer and raising the song of praise in acknowledgment of divine care during the day.

Fathers and mothers, however pressing your business, do not fail to gather your family around God's altar. Ask for the guardianship of holy angels in your home. Remember that your dear ones are exposed to temptations. Daily annoyances beset the path of young and old. Those who would live patient, loving, cheerful lives must pray. Only by receiving constant help from God can we gain the victory over self.

Home should be a place where cheerfulness, courtesy, and love abide; and where these graces dwell, there will abide happiness and peace. Troubles may invade, but these are the lot of humanity. Let patience, gratitude, and love keep sunshine in the heart, though the day may be ever so cloudy. In such homes angels of God abide.

Confidence Between Husband and Wife

Let the husband and wife study each other's happiness, never failing in the small courtesies and little kindly acts that cheer and brighten the life. Perfect confidence should exist between husband and wife. Together they should consider their responsibilities. Together they should work for the highest good of their children. Never should they in the presence of the children criticize each other's plans or question each other's judgment. Let the wife be careful not to make the husband's work for the children more difficult. Let the husband hold up the hands of his wife, giving her wise counsel and loving encouragement.

No barrier of coldness and reserve should be allowed to arise between parents and children. Let parents become acquainted with their children, seeking to understand their tastes and dispositions, entering into their feelings, and drawing out what is in their hearts.

Parents, let your children see that you love them, and will do all in your power to make them happy. If you do so, your necessary restrictions will have far greater weight in their young minds. Rule your children with tenderness and compassion, remembering that "their angels do always behold the face of My Father which is in heaven." Matthew 18:10. If you desire the angels to do for your children the work given them of God, cooperate with them by doing your part.

Ready to Leave Home

Brought up under the wise and loving guidance of a true home, children will have no desire to wander away in search of pleasure and companionship. Evil will not attract them. The spirit that prevails in the home will mold their characters; they will form habits and principles that will be a strong defense against temptation when they shall leave the home shelter and take their place in the world.

Children as well as parents have important duties in the home. They should be taught that they are a part of the home firm. They are fed and clothed and loved and cared for; and they should respond to these many mercies by bearing their share of the home burdens, and bringing all the happiness possible into the family of which they are members.

Children are sometimes tempted to chafe under restraint; but in afterlife they will bless their parents for the faithful care and strict watchfulness that guarded and guided them in their years of inexperience.

Education Begins at Home

OUR children stand, as it were, at the parting of the ways. On every hand the world's enticements to self-seeking and self-indulgence call them away from the path cast up for the ransomed of the Lord. Whether their lives shall be a blessing or a curse depends upon the choice they make. Overflowing with energy, eager to test their untried capabilities, they must find some outlet for their superabounding life. Active they will be for good or for evil.

God's Word does not repress activity, but guides it aright. God does not bid the youth to be less aspiring. The elements of character that make a man truly successful and honored among men—the irrepressible desire for some greater good, the indomitable will, the strenuous application, the untiring perseverance—are not to be discouraged. By the grace of God they are to be directed to the attainment of objects as much higher than mere selfish and worldly interests as the heavens are higher than the earth.

Parents' First Duty

With us as parents and as Christians it rests to give our children right direction. They are to be carefully, wisely, tenderly guided into paths of Christlike ministry. We are under sacred covenant with God to rear our children for

His service. To surround them with such influences as shall lead them to choose a life of service, and to give them the training needed, is our first duty.

"God so loved, . . . that He gave"—"gave His only-begotten Son," that we should not perish, but have everlasting life. "Christ also hath loved us, and hath given Himself for us." John 3:16; Ephesians 5:2. If we love, we shall give. "Not to be ministered unto, but to minister" (Matthew 20:28), is the great lesson which we are to learn and to teach.

Let the youth be impressed with the thought that they are not their own. They belong to Christ. They are the purchase of His blood, the claim of His love. They live because He keeps them by His power. Their time, their strength, their capabilities are His, to be developed, to be trained, to be used for Him.

Next to the angelic beings, the human family, formed in the image of God, are the noblest of His created works. God desires them to become all that He has made it possible for them to be, and to do their very best with the powers He has given them.

Life is mysterious and sacred. It is the manifestation of God Himself, the source of all life. Precious are its opportunities, and earnestly should they be improved. Once lost they are gone forever.

Before us God places eternity with its solemn realities, and gives us a grasp on immortal, imperishable themes. He presents valuable, ennobling truth, that we may advance in a safe and sure path, in pursuit of an object worthy of the earnest engagement of all our capabilities.

God looks into the tiny seed that He Himself has

formed, and sees wrapped within it the beautiful flower, the shrub, or the lofty, wide-spreading tree. So does He see the possibilities in every human being. We are here for a purpose. God has given us His plan for our life, and He desires us to reach the highest standard of development.

He desires that we shall constantly be growing in holiness, in happiness, in usefulness. All have capabilities which they must be taught to regard as sacred endowments, to appreciate as the Lord's gifts, and rightly to employ. He desires the youth to cultivate every power of their being, and to bring every faculty into active exercise. He desires them to enjoy all that is useful and precious in this life, to be good and to do good, laying up a heavenly treasure for the future life.

It should be their ambition to excel in all things that are unselfish, high, and noble. Let them look to Christ as the pattern after which they are to be fashioned. The holy ambition that He revealed in His life they are to cherish—an ambition to make the world better for their having lived in it. This is the work to which they are called.

An Equal Education

A comprehensive education is needed—an education that will demand from parents and teachers such thought and effort as mere instruction in the sciences does not require. Something more is called for than the culture of the intellect. Education is not complete unless the body, the mind, and the heart are equally educated. The character must receive proper discipline for its fullest and highest development. All the faculties of mind and body are to be developed and rightly trained.

True education includes the whole being. It teaches the right use of one's self. It enables us to make the best use of brain, bone, and muscle, of body, mind, and heart. The faculties of the mind, as the higher powers, are to rule the kingdom of the body. The natural appetites and passions are to be brought under the control of the conscience and the spiritual affections. Christ stands at the head of humanity, and it is His purpose to lead us, in His service, into high and holy paths of purity. By the wondrous working of His grace, we are to be made complete in Him.

Jesus secured His education in the home. His mother was His first human teacher. From her lips, and from the scrolls of the prophets, He learned of heavenly things. He lived in a peasant's home, and faithfully and cheerfully acted His part in bearing the household burdens. He who had been the Commander of heaven was a willing Servant, a loving, obedient Son. He learned a trade, and with His own hands worked in the carpenter's shop with Joseph. In the garb of a common laborer, He walked the streets of the little town, going to and returning from His humble work.

With the people of that age the value of things was estimated by outward show. As religion had declined in power, it had increased in pomp. The educators of the time sought to command respect by display and ostentation. To all this the life of Jesus presented a marked contrast. His life demonstrated the worthlessness of those things that men regarded as life's great essentials. The schools of His time, with their magnifying of things small and their belittling of things great, He did not seek. His education was gained from heaven-appointed sources, from useful work, from the study of the Scriptures, from nature, and from the experiences of life—God's lesson books, full of instruction to all who bring to them the willing hand, the seeing eye, and the understanding heart.

"The Child grew, and waxed strong in spirit, filled with wisdom: and the grace of God was upon Him." Luke 2:40.

Thus prepared, He went forth to His mission, in every moment of His contact with men exerting upon them an influence to bless, a power to transform, such as the world had never witnessed.

The Child's First School

The home is the child's first school, and it is here that the foundation should be laid for a life of service. Its principles are to be taught not merely in theory. They are to shape the whole life training.

Very early the lesson of helpfulness should be taught the child. As soon as strength and reasoning power are sufficiently developed, he should be given duties to perform in the home. He should be encouraged in trying to help father and mother, encouraged to deny and to control himself, to put others' happiness and convenience before his own, to watch for opportunities to cheer and assist brothers and sisters and playmates, and to show kindness to the aged, the sick, and the unfortunate. The more fully the spirit of true ministry pervades the home, the more fully it will be developed in the lives of the children. They will learn to find joy in service and sacrifice for the good of others.

The home training should be supplemented by the work of the school. The development of the whole being, physical, mental, and spiritual, and the teaching of service and sacrifice, should be kept constantly in view.

Above any other agency, service for Christ's sake in the little things of everyday experience has power to mold the character and to direct the life into lines of unselfish ministry. To awaken this spirit, to encourage, and rightly to direct it, is the parent's and the teacher's work. No more important work could be committed to them. The spirit of ministry is the spirit of heaven, and with every effort to develop and encourage it angels will cooperate.

Such an education must be based upon the Word of God. Here only are its principles given in their fullness. The Bible should be made the foundation of study and of teaching. The essential knowledge is a knowledge of God and of Him whom He has sent.

"Know Thyself"

Every child and every youth should have a knowledge of himself. He should understand the physical habitation that God has given him, and the laws by which it is kept in health. All should be thoroughly grounded in the common branches of education. And they should have industrial training that will make them men and women of practical ability, fitted for the duties of everyday life. To this should be added training and practical experience in various lines of missionary effort.

Let the youth advance as fast and as far as they can in the acquisition of knowledge. Let their field of study be as broad as their powers can compass. And as they learn, let them impart their knowledge. It is thus that their minds will acquire discipline and power. It is the use they make of knowledge that determines the value of their education. To spend a long time in study, with no effort to impart what

51

is gained, often proves a hindrance rather than a help to real development. In both the home and the school it should be the student's effort to learn how to study and how to impart the knowledge gained. Whatever his calling, he is to be both a learner and a teacher as long as life shall last. Thus he may advance continually, making God his trust, clinging to Him who is infinite in wisdom, who can reveal the secrets hidden for ages, who can solve the most difficult problems for minds that believe in Him.

Influence of Association

God's Word places great stress upon the influence of association, even upon men and women. How much greater is its power on the developing mind and character of children and youth. The company they keep, the principles they adopt, the habits they form, will decide the question of their usefulness here, and of their future, eternal interest.

It is a terrible fact, and one that should make the hearts of parents tremble, that in so many schools and colleges to which the youth are sent for mental culture and discipline, influences prevail which misshape the character, divert the mind from life's true aims, and debase the morals. Through contact with the irreligious, the pleasure loving, and the corrupt, many, many youth lose the simplicity and purity, the faith in God, and the spirit of self-sacrifice that Christian fathers and mothers have cherished and guarded by careful instruction and earnest prayer.

Many who enter school with the purpose of fitting themselves for some line of unselfish ministry, become absorbed in secular studies. An ambition is aroused to win distinction in scholarship and to gain position and honor in the world.

The purpose for which they entered school is lost sight of, and the life is given up to selfish and worldly pursuits. And often habits are formed that ruin the life both for this world and for the world to come.

As a rule, men and women who have broad ideas, unselfish purposes, noble aspirations, are those in whom these characteristics were developed by their associations in early years. In all His dealings with Israel, God urged upon them the importance of guarding the associations of their children. All the arrangements of civil, religious, and social life were made with a view to preserving the children from harmful companionship, and making them, from their earliest years, familiar with the precepts and principles of the law of God. The object lesson given at the birth of the nation was of a nature deeply to impress all hearts. Before the last terrible judgment came upon the Egyptians in the death of the firstborn, God commanded His people to gather their children into their own homes. The doorpost of every house was marked with blood, and within the protection assured by this token all were to abide. So today parents who love and fear God are to keep their children under "the bond of the covenant"—within the protection of those sacred influences made possible through Christ's redeeming blood.

All who are seeking to work in harmony with God's plan of education will have His sustaining grace, His continual presence, His keeping power. To everyone He says:

"Be strong and of a good courage; be not afraid, neither be thou dismayed: for the Lord thy God is with thee." "I will not fail thee, nor forsake thee." Joshua 1:9, 5.

53

What Shall the Child Read?

THE mastermind in the confederacy of evil is ever working to keep out of sight the words of God, and to bring into view the opinions of men. He means that we shall not hear the voice of God saying, "This is the way, walk ye in it." Isaiah 30:21. Through perverted educational processes he is doing his utmost to obscure heaven's light.

Philosophical speculation and scientific research in which God is not acknowledged are making skeptics of thousands. In the schools of today the conclusions that learned men have reached as the result of their scientific investigations are carefully taught and fully explained, while the impression is distinctly given that if these learned men are correct, the Bible cannot be. Skepticism is attractive to the human mind. The youth see in it an independence that captivates the imagination, and they are deceived. Satan triumphs. He nourishes every seed of doubt that is sown in young hearts. He causes it to grow and bear fruit, and soon a plentiful harvest of infidelity is reaped.

It is because the human heart is inclined to evil that it is so dangerous to sow the seeds of skepticism in young minds. Whatever weakens faith in God robs the soul of power to resist temptation. It removes the only real safeguard against sin. We are in need of schools where the youth shall be taught that greatness consists in honoring God by revealing His character in daily life. Through His Word and His works we need to learn of God, that our lives may fulfill His purpose.

The True Source of Light

In order to obtain an education, many think it essential to study the writings of infidel authors, because these works contain many bright gems of thought. But who was the originator of these gems of thought? It was God, and God only. He is the source of all light. Why then should we wade through the mass of error contained in the works of infidels for the sake of a few intellectual truths, when all truth is at our command?

How is it that men who are at war with the government of God come into possession of the wisdom which they sometimes display? Satan himself was educated in the heavenly courts, and he has a knowledge of good as well as of evil. He mingles the precious with the vile, and this is what gives him power to deceive. But because Satan has robed himself in garments of heavenly brightness, shall we receive him as an angel of light? The tempter has his agents, educated according to his methods, inspired by his spirit, and adapted to his work. Shall we cooperate with them? Shall we receive the works of his agents as essential to the acquirement of an education?

If the time and effort spent in seeking to grasp the bright ideas of infidels were given to studying the precious things of the Word of God, thousands who now sit in darkness and in the shadow of death would be rejoicing in the glory of the Light of life.

As I see libraries filled with ponderous volumes of historical and theological lore, I think, Why spend money for that which is not bread? The sixth chapter of John tells us more than can be found in such works. Christ says: "I am the Bread of Life: he that cometh to Me shall never hunger; and he that believeth on Me shall never thirst." "I am the living Bread which came down from heaven: if any man eat of this bread, he shall live forever." "He that believeth on Me hath everlasting life." "The words that I speak unto you, they are spirit, and they are life." John 6:35, 51, 47, 63.

God and History

There is a study of history that is not to be condemned. Sacred history was one of the studies in the schools of the prophets. In the record of His dealings with the nations were traced the footsteps of Jehovah. So today we are to consider the dealings of God with the nations of the earth. We are to see in history the fulfillment of prophecy, to study the workings of Providence in the great reformatory movements, and to understand the progress of events in the marshaling of the nations for the final conflict of the great controversy.

Such study will give broad, comprehensive views of life. It will help us to understand something of its relations and dependencies, how wonderfully we are bound together in the great brotherhood of society and nations, and to how great an extent the oppression and degradation of one member means loss to all.

But history, as commonly studied, is concerned with man's achievements, his victories in battle, his success in attaining power and greatness. God's agency in the affairs of men is lost sight of. Few study the working out of His purpose in the rise and fall of nations.

Many of the popular publications of the day are filled with sensational stories that are educating the youth in wickedness and leading them in the path to perdition. Mere children in years are old in a knowledge of crime. They are incited to evil by the tales they read. In imagination they act over the deeds portrayed, until their ambition is aroused to see what they can do in committing crime and evading punishment.

To the active minds of children and youth, the scenes pictured in imaginary revelations of the future are realities. As revolutions are predicted, and all manner of proceedings described that break down the barriers of law and self-restraint, many catch the spirit of these representations. They are led to the commission of crimes even worse, if possible, than these sensational writers depict. Through such influences as these, society is becoming demoralized. The seeds of lawlesssness are sown broadcast. None need marvel that a harvest of crime is the result.

Beneath the Veil

Works of romance, frivolous, exciting tales, are, in hardly less degree, a curse to the reader. The author may profess to teach a moral lesson, throughout his work he may interweave religious sentiments; but often these serve only to veil the folly and worthlessness beneath.

The world is flooded with books that are filled with enticing error. The youth receive as truth that which the Bible denounces as falsehood, and they love and cling to deception that means ruin to the soul.

57

There are works of fiction that were written for the purpose of teaching truth or exposing some great evil. Some of these works have accomplished good. Yet they have also wrought untold harm. They contain statements and highly wrought pen pictures that excite the imagination and give rise to a train of thought which is full of danger, especially to the youth. The scenes described are lived over and over again in their thoughts. Such reading unfits the mind for usefulness and disqualifies it for spiritual exercise. It destroys interest in the Bible. Heavenly things find little place in the thoughts. As the mind dwells upon the scenes of impurity portrayed, passion is aroused, and the end is sin.

Books Filled With Falsehood.

In the education of children and youth, fairy tales, myths, and fictitious stories are now given a large place. Books of this character are used in the schools, and they are to be found in many homes. How can Christian parents permit their children to use books so filled with falsehood? When the children ask the meaning of stories so contrary to the teaching of their parents, the answer is that the stories are not true; but this does not do away with the evil results of their use. The ideas presented in these books mislead the children. They impart false views of life, and beget and foster a desire for the unreal.

The widespread use of such books at this time is one of the cunning devices of Satan. He is seeking to divert the minds of old and young from the great work of character building. He means that our children and youth shall be swept away by the soul-destroying deceptions with which he is filling the world. Therefore he seeks to divert their minds from the Word of God, and thus prevent them from obtaining a knowledge of those truths that would be their safeguard.

Never should books containing a perversion of truth be placed in the hands of children or youth. Let not our children, in the very process of obtaining an education, receive ideas that will prove to be seeds of sin. If those with mature minds had nothing to do with such books, they would themselves be far safer, and their example and influence on the right side would make it far less difficult to guard the youth from temptation.

We have an abundance of that which is real, that which is divine. Those who thirst for knowledge need not go to polluted fountains. The Lord says:

"Bow down thine ear, and hear the words of the wise,
And apply thine heart unto My knowledge. . . .
That thy trust may be in the Lord,
I have made known to thee this day, even to thee.
Have not I written to thee excellent things
In counsels and knowledge,
That I might make thee know the certainty of the words of
    truth;
That thou mightest answer the words of truth to them that
    send unto thee?"

Proverbs 22:17-21.

The Purest Streams of Knowledge

So also Christ presented the principles of truth in the gospel. In His teaching we may drink of the pure streams that flow from the throne of God. Christ could have imparted to men knowledge that would have surpassed any previous disclosures, and put in the background every other dis-

59

covery. He could have unlocked mystery after mystery, and could have concentrated around these wonderful revelations the active, earnest thought of successive generations till the close of time. But He would not spare a moment from teaching the science of salvation. His time, His faculties, and His life were appreciated and used only as the means for working out the salvation of the souls of men. He had come to seek and to save that which was lost, and He would not be turned from His purpose. He allowed nothing to divert Him.

Christ imparted only that knowledge which could be utilized. His instruction of the people was confined to the needs of their own condition in practical life. The curiosity that led them to come to Him with prying questions, He did not gratify. All such questionings He made the occasion for solemn, earnest, vital appeals. To those who were so eager to pluck from the tree of knowledge, He offered the fruit of the tree of life. They found every avenue closed, except the way that leads to God. Every fountain was sealed, save the fountain of eternal life.

Our Saviour did not encourage any to attend the rabbinical schools of His day, for the reason that their minds would be corrupted with the continually repeated, "They say," or, "It has been said." Why, then, should we accept the unstable words of men as exalted wisdom, when a greater, a certain, wisdom is at our command?

That which I have seen of eternal things, and that which I have seen of the weakness of humanity, has deeply impressed my mind, and influenced my lifework. I see nothing wherein man should be praised or glorified. I see no reason why the opinions of worldly wisemen and so-called great

60

men should be trusted in and exalted. How can those who are destitute of divine enlightenment have correct ideas of God's plans and ways? They either deny Him altogether and ignore His existence, or they circumscribe His power by their own finite conceptions.

Let us choose to be taught by Him who created the heavens and the earth, by Him who set the stars in their order in the firmament, and appointed the sun and the moon to do their work.

Highest Development of the Mind

It is right for the youth to feel that they must reach the highest development of their mental powers. We would not restrict the education to which God has set no limit. But our attainments avail nothing if not put to use for the honor of God and the good of humanity.

It is not well to crowd the mind with studies that require intense application, but that are not brought into use in practical life. Such education will be a loss to the student. For these studies lessen his desire and inclination for the studies that would fit him for usefulness and enable him to fulfill his responsibilities. A practical training is worth far more than any amount of mere theorizing. It is not enough even to have knowledge. We must have ability to use the knowledge aright.

The time, means, and study that so many expend for a comparatively useless education should be devoted to gaining an education that would make them practical men and women, fitted to bear life's responsibilities. Such an education would be of the highest value.

What we need is knowledge that will strengthen mind

61

and soul, that will make us better men and women. Heart education is of far more importance than mere book learning. It is well, even essential, to have a knowledge of the world in which we live; but if we leave eternity out of our reckoning, we shall make a failure from which we can never recover.

A student may devote all his powers to acquiring knowledge; but unless he has a knowledge of God, unless he obeys the laws that govern his own being, he will destroy himself. By wrong habits, he loses the power of self-appreciation; he loses self-control. He cannot reason correctly about matters that concern him most deeply. He is reckless and irrational in his treatment of mind and body. Through his neglect to cultivate right principles, he is ruined both for this world and for the world to come.

If the youth understood their own weakness, they would find in God their strength. If they seek to be taught by Him, they will become wise in His wisdom, and their lives will be fruitful of blessing to the world. But if they give up their minds to mere worldly and speculative study, and thus separate from God, they will lose all that enriches life.

Health Begins at Home

THE knowledge that man is to be a temple for God, a habitation for the revealing of His glory, should be the highest incentive to the care and development of our physical powers. Fearfully and wonderfully has the Creator wrought in the human frame, and He bids us make it our study, understand its needs, and act our part in preserving it from harm and defilement.

In order to have good health we must have good blood, for the blood is the current of life. It repairs waste and nourishes the body. When supplied with the proper food elements and when cleansed and vitalized by contact with pure air, it carries life and vigor to every part of the system. The more perfect the circulation, the better will this work be accomplished.

At every pulsation of the heart the blood should make its way quickly and easily to all parts of the body. Its circulation should not be hindered by tight clothing or bands, or by insufficient clothing of the extremities. Whatever hinders the circulation forces the blood back to the vital organs, producing congestion. Headache, cough, palpitation of the heart, or indigestion is often the result.

In order to have good blood, we must breathe well. Full, deep inspirations of pure air, which fill the lungs with oxy-

63

gen, purify the blood. They impart to it a bright color, and send it, a life-giving current, to every part of the body. A good respiration soothes the nerves; it stimulates the appetite, and renders digestion more perfect; and it induces sound, refreshing sleep.

Good Breathing Habits

The lungs should be allowed the greatest freedom possible. Their capacity is developed by free action. It diminishes if they are cramped and compressed; hence the ill effects of the practice so common, especially in sedentary pursuits, of stooping at one's work. In this position it is impossible to breathe deeply.

The lungs are constantly throwing off impurities, and they need to be constantly supplied with fresh air. Impure air does not afford the necessary supply of oxygen, and the blood passes to the brain and other organs without being vitalized. Hence the necessity of thorough ventilation. To live in close, ill-ventilated rooms, where the air is dead and vitiated, weakens the entire system. It becomes peculiarly sensitive to the influence of cold, and a slight exposure induces disease. It is close confinement indoors that makes many women pale and feeble. They breathe the same air over and over until it becomes laden with poisonous matter thrown off through the lungs and pores, and impurities are thus conveyed back to the blood.

In the construction of buildings, whether for public purposes or as dwellings, care should be taken to provide for good ventilation and plenty of sunlight. Churches and schoolrooms are often faulty in this respect. Neglect of proper ventilation is responsible for much of the drowsiness and dullness that destroy the effect of many a sermon and make the teacher's work toilsome and ineffective.

So far as possible, all buildings intended for human habitation should be placed on high, well-drained ground. This will ensure a dry site, and prevent the danger of disease from dampness and miasma. This matter is often too lightly regarded. Continuous ill health, serious diseases, and many deaths result from the dampness and malaria of low-lying, ill-drained situations.

In the building of houses it is especially important to secure thorough ventilation and plenty of sunlight. Let there be a current of air and an abundance of light in every room in the house. Sleeping rooms should be so arranged as to have a free circulation of air day and night. No room is fit to be occupied as a sleeping room unless it can be thrown open daily to the air and sunshine.

Choosing the Homesite

In building, many make careful provision for their plants and flowers. The greenhouse or window devoted to their use is warm and sunny; for without warmth, air, and sunshine, plants would not live and flourish. If these conditions are necessary to the life of plants, how much more necessary are they for our own health and that of our families and guests!

If we would have our homes the abiding place of health and happiness, we must place them above the miasma and fog of the lowlands, and give free entrance to heaven's life-giving agencies. Dispense with heavy curtains, open the windows and the blinds, allow no vines, however beautiful, to shade the windows, and permit no trees to stand so near

65

the house as to shut out the sunshine. The sunlight may fade the drapery and the carpets, and tarnish the picture frames; but it will bring a healthy glow to the cheeks of the children.

Those who have the aged to provide for should remember that these especially need warm, comfortable rooms. Vigor declines as years advance, leaving less vitality with which to resist unhealthful influences; hence the greater necessity for the aged to have plenty of sunlight, and fresh, pure air.

Scrupulous cleanliness is essential to both physical and mental health. Impurities are constantly thrown off from the body through the skin. Its millions of pores are quickly clogged unless kept clean by frequent bathing, and the impurities which should pass off through the skin become an additional burden to the other eliminating organs.

Most persons would receive benefit from a cool or tepid bath every day, morning or evening. Instead of increasing the liability to take cold, a bath, properly taken, fortifies against cold, because it improves the circulation; the blood is brought to the surface, and a more easy and regular flow is obtained. The mind and the body are alike invigorated. The muscles become more flexible, the intellect is made brighter. The bath is a soother of the nerves. Bathing helps the bowels, the stomach, and the liver, giving health and energy to each, and it promotes digestion.

It is important also that the clothing be kept clean. The garments worn absorb the waste matter that passes off through the pores; if they are not frequently changed and washed, the impurities will be reabsorbed.

Every form of uncleanliness tends to disease. Death-producing germs abound in dark, neglected corners, in decaying refuse, in dampness and mold and must. No waste vegetables or heaps of fallen leaves should be allowed to remain near the house, to decay and poison the air. Nothing unclean or decaying should be tolerated within the home. In towns or cities regarded perfectly healthful, many an epidemic of fever has been traced to decaying matter about the dwelling of some careless householder.

Perfect cleanliness, plenty of sunlight, careful attention to sanitation in every detail of the home life, are essential to freedom from disease and to the cheerfulness and vigor of the inmates of the home.

Feeding the Family

OUR bodies are built up from the food we eat. There is a constant breaking down of the tissues of the body; every movement of every organ involves waste, and this waste is repaired from our food. Each organ of the body requires its share of nutrition. The brain must be supplied with its portion; the bones, muscles, and nerves demand theirs. It is a wonderful process that transforms the food into blood, and uses this blood to build up the varied parts of the body; but this process is going on continually, supplying with life and strength each nerve, muscle, and tissue.

Those foods should be chosen that best supply the elements needed for building up the body. In this choice, appetite is not a safe guide. Through wrong habits of eating the appetite has become perverted. Often it demands food that impairs health and causes weakness instead of strength. We cannot safely be guided by the customs of society. The disease and suffering that everywhere prevail are largely due to popular errors in regard to diet.

In order to know what are the best foods, we must study God's original plan for man's diet. He who created man and who understands his needs appointed Adam his food. "Behold," He said, "I have given you every herb yielding seed, . . . and every tree, in which is the fruit of a tree yielding

68

seed; to you it shall be for food." Genesis 1:29, A.R.V. Upon leaving Eden to gain his livelihood by tilling the earth under the curse of sin, man received permission to eat also "the herb of the field." Genesis 3:18.

Foods for Life

Grains, fruits, nuts, and vegetables constitute the diet chosen for us by our Creator. These foods, prepared in as simple and natural a manner as possible, are the most healthful and nourishing. They impart a strength, a power of endurance, and a vigor of intellect that are not afforded by a more complex and stimulating diet.

But not all foods wholesome in themselves are equally suited to our needs under all circumstances. Care should be taken in the selection of food. Our diet should be suited to the season, to the climate in which we live, and to the occupation we follow. Some foods that are adapted for use at one season or in one climate are not suited to another. So there are different foods best suited for persons in different occupations. Often food that can be used with benefit by those engaged in hard physical labor is unsuitable for persons of sedentary pursuits or intense mental application. God has given us an ample variety of healthful foods and each person should choose from it the things that experience and sound judgment prove to be best suited to his own necessities.

Nature's abundant supply of fruits, nuts, and grains is ample, and year by year the products of all lands are more generally distributed to all by the increased facilities for transportation. As a result many articles of food which a few years ago were regarded as expensive luxuries, are now within the reach of all as foods for everyday use. This is especially the case with dried and canned fruits.

Nuts and nut foods are coming largely into use to take the place of flesh meats. With nuts may be combined grains, fruits, and some roots, to make foods that are healthful and nourishing. Care should be taken, however, not to use too large a proportion of nuts. Those who realize ill effects from the use of nut foods may find the difficulty removed by attending to this precaution. It should be remembered, too, that some nuts are not so wholesome as others. Almonds are preferable to peanuts, but peanuts in limited quantities, used in connection with grains, are nourishing and digestible.

When properly prepared, olives, like nuts, supply the place of butter and flesh meats. The oil as eaten in the olive is far preferable to animal oil or fat. It serves as a laxative. Its use will be found beneficial to tuberculosis patients, and it is healing to an inflamed, irritated stomach.

New Eating Habits

Persons who have accustomed themselves to a rich, highly stimulating diet, have an unnatural taste, and they cannot at once relish food that is plain and simple. It will take time for the taste to become natural and for the stomach to recover from the abuse it has suffered. But those who persevere in the use of wholesome food will, after a time, find it palatable. Its delicate and delicious flavors will be appreciated, and it will be eaten with greater enjoyment than can be derived from unwholesome dainties. And the stomach in a healthy condition, neither fevered nor overtaxed, can readily perform its task.

In order to maintain health, a sufficient supply of good, nourishing food is needed. If we plan wisely, that which is most conducive to health can be secured in almost every land. The various preparations of rice, wheat, corn, and oats are sent abroad everywhere, also beans, peas, and lentils. These, with native or imported fruits, and the variety of vegetables that grow in each locality, give an opportunity to select a dietary that is complete without the use of flesh meats.

Wherever fruit can be grown in abundance, a liberal supply should be prepared for winter by canning or drying. Small fruits, such as currants, gooseberries, strawberries, raspberries, and blackberries, can be grown to advantage in many places where they are but little used and their cultivation is neglected.

It is especially necessary that the fruit for canning should be in good condition. Use little sugar, and cook the fruit only long enough to ensure its preservation. Thus prepared, it is an excellent substitute for fresh fruit.

Wherever dried fruits, such as raisins, prunes, apples pears, peaches, and apricots, are obtainable at moderate prices, it will be found that they can be used as staple articles of diet much more freely than is customary, with the best results to the health and vigor of all classes of workers.

Intelligent Food Preparation

There should not be a great variety at any one meal, for this encourages overeating, and causes indigestion.

It is not well to eat fruit and vegetables at the same meal. If the digestion is feeble, the use of both will often cause distress and inability to put forth mental effort. It is better to

71

have the fruit at one meal and the vegetables at another.

The meals should be varied. The same dishes prepared in the same way should not appear on the table meal after meal and day after day. The meals are eaten with greater relish, and the system is better nourished, when the food is varied.

It is wrong to eat merely to gratify the appetite, but no indifference should be manifested regarding the quality of the food or the manner of its preparation. If the food eaten is not relished, the body will not be so well nourished. The food should be carefully chosen and prepared with intelligence and skill.

For use in bread making, the superfine white flour is not the best. Its use is neither healthful nor economical. Fine-flour bread is lacking in nutritive elements to be found in bread made from the whole wheat. It is a frequent cause of constipation and other unhealthful conditions.

Zwieback, or twice-baked bread, is one of the most easily digested and most palatable of foods. Let ordinary raised bread be cut in slices and dried in a warm oven till the last trace of moisture disappears. Then let it be browned slightly all the way through. In a dry place this bread can be kept much longer than ordinary bread, and, if reheated before using, it will be as fresh as when new.

Far too much sugar is ordinarily used in food. Cakes, sweet puddings, pastries, jellies, jams, are active causes of indigestion. Especially harmful are the custards and puddings in which milk, eggs, and sugar are the chief ingredients. The free use of milk and sugar taken together should be avoided.

Scanty, ill-cooked food depraves the blood by weaken-

72

ing the blood-making organs. It deranges the system, and brings on disease, with its accompaniment of irritable nerves and bad tempers. The victims of poor cookery are numbered by thousands and tens of thousands. Over many graves might be written: "Died because of poor cooking," "Died of an abused stomach."

Cooking, No Mean Science

It is a sacred duty for those who cook to learn how to prepare healthful food. Many souls are lost as the result of poor cookery. It takes thought and care to make good bread; but there is more religion in a loaf of good bread than many think. There are few really good cooks. Young women think that it is menial to cook and do other kinds of housework; and, for this reason, many girls who marry and have the care of families have little idea of the duties devolving upon a wife and mother.

Cooking is no mean science, and it is one of the most essential in practical life. It is a science that all women should learn, and it should be taught in a way to benefit the poorer classes. To make food appetizing and at the same time simple and nourishing, requires skill; but it can be done. Cooks should know how to prepare simple food in a simple and healthful manner and so that it will be found more palatable, as well as more wholesome, because of its simplicity.

Every woman who is at the head of a family and yet does not understand the art of healthful cookery should determine to learn that which is so essential to the well-being of her household. In many places cooking schools afford opportunity for instruction in this line. She who has not the help of such facilities should put herself under the instruction of some good cook, and persevere in her efforts for improvement until she is mistress of the culinary art.

Regularity in eating is of vital importance. There should be a specified time for each meal. At this time, let everyone eat what the system requires, and then take nothing more until the next meal. There are many who eat when the system needs no food, at irregular intervals, and between meals, because they have not sufficient strength of will to resist inclination. When traveling, some are constantly nibbling if anything eatable is within their reach. This is very injurious. If travelers would eat regularly of food that is simple and nutritious, they would not feel so great weariness, nor suffer so much from sickness.

When Not to Eat

Another pernicious habit is that of eating just before bedtime. The regular meals may have been taken; but because there is a sense of faintness more food is eaten. By indulgence, this wrong practice becomes a habit, and often so firmly fixed that it is thought impossible to sleep without food. As a result of eating late suppers, the digestive process is continued through the sleeping hours. But though the stomach works constantly, its work is not properly accomplished. The sleep is often disturbed with unpleasant dreams, and in the morning the person awakes unrefreshed, and with little relish for breakfast. When we lie down to rest, the stomach should have its work all done, that it, as well as the other organs of the body, may enjoy rest. For persons of sedentary habits, late suppers are particularly

74

harmful. With them the disturbance created is often the beginning of disease that ends in death.

In many cases the faintness that leads to a desire for food is felt because the digestive organs have been too severely taxed during the day. After disposing of one meal, the digestive organs need rest. At least five or six hours should intervene between the meals; and most persons who give the plan a trial will find that two meals a day are better than three.

Food should not be eaten very hot or very cold. If food is cold, the vital force of the stomach is drawn upon in order to warm it before digestion can take place. Cold drinks are injurious for the same reason; while the free use of hot drinks is debilitating. In fact, the more liquid there is taken with the meals, the more difficult it is for the food to digest; for the liquid must be absorbed before digestion can begin.

Do not eat largely of salt, avoid the use of pickles and spiced foods, eat an abundance of fruit, and the irritation that calls for so much drink at mealtime will largely disappear.

Food should be eaten slowly, and should be thoroughly masticated. This is necessary in order that the saliva may be properly mixed with the food and the digestive fluids be called into action.

Another serious evil is eating at improper times, as after violent or excessive exercise, when one is much exhausted or heated. Immediately after eating there is a strong draft upon the nervous energies; and when mind or body is heavily taxed just before or just after eating, digestion is hindered. When one is excited, anxious, or hurried it is better not to eat until rest or relief is found.

The stomach is closely related to the brain; and when the stomach is diseased, the nerve power is called from the brain to the aid of the weakened digestive organs. When these demands are too frequent, the brain becomes congested. When the brain is constantly taxed, and there is lack of physical exercise, even plain food should be eaten sparingly. At mealtime cast off care and anxious thought; do not feel hurried, but eat slowly and with cheerfulness, with your heart filled with gratitude to God for all His blessings.

Surplus Food

Many think that because their food is simple and wholesome they may indulge appetite without restraint, and they eat to excess, sometimes to gluttony. This is an error. The digestive organs should not be burdened with a quantity or quality of food which it will tax the system to appropriate.

Sometimes the result of overeating is felt at once. In other cases there is no sensation of pain; but the digestive organs lose their vital force, and the foundation of physical strength is undermined.

The surplus food burdens the system, and produces morbid, feverish conditions. It calls an undue amount of blood to the stomach, causing the limbs and extremities to chill quickly. It lays a heavy tax on the digestive organs, and when these organs have accomplished their task, there is a feeling of faintness or languor. Some who are continually overeating call this all-gone feeling hunger; but it is caused by the overworked condition of the digestive organs. At times there is numbness of the brain, with disinclination to mental or physical effort.

These unpleasant symptoms are felt because nature has

accomplished her work at an unnecessary outlay of vital force, and is thoroughly exhausted. The stomach is saying, "Give me rest." But with many the faintness is interpreted as a demand for more food; so instead of giving the stomach rest, another burden is placed upon it. As a consequence the digestive organs are often worn out when they should be capable of doing good work.

We should not provide for the Sabbath a more liberal supply or a greater variety of food than for other days. Instead of this, the food should be more simple, and less should be eaten, in order that the mind may be clear and vigorous to comprehend spiritual things. A clogged stomach means a clogged brain. The most precious words may be heard and not appreciated, because the mind is confused by an improper diet. By overeating on the Sabbath, many do more than they think to unfit themselves for receiving the benefit of its sacred opportunities.

Let the meals, however simple, be palatable and attractive. Especially in families where there are children, it is well, on the Sabbath, to provide something that will be regarded as a treat, something the family do not have every day.

Where wrong habits of diet have been indulged, there should be no delay in reform. It is not easy to prescribe rules that will meet every case; but with attention to right principles in eating, great reforms may be made, and the cook need not be continually toiling to tempt the appetite.

Abstemiousness in diet is rewarded with mental and moral vigor; it also aids in the control of the passions. Overeating is especially harmful to those who are sluggish in temperament; these should eat sparingly, and take plenty of physical exercise. There are men and women of excellent natural ability who do not accomplish half what they might if they would exercise self-control in the denial of appetite.

Many writers and speakers fail here. After eating heartily, they give themselves to sedentary occupations, reading, study, or writing, allowing no time for physical exercise. As a consequence, the free flow of thought and words is checked. They cannot write or speak with the force and intensity necessary in order to reach the heart; their efforts are tame and fruitless.

Those upon whom rest important responsibilities, those, above all, who are guardians of spiritual interests, should be men of keen feeling and quick perception. More than others they need to be temperate in eating. Rich and luxurious food should have no place upon their tables.

Every day men in positions of trust have decisions to make upon which depend results of great importance. Often they have to think rapidly, and this can be done successfully by those only who practice strict temperance. The mind strengthens under the correct treatment of the physical and mental powers. If the strain is not too great, new vigor comes with every taxation. But often the work of those who have important plans to consider and important decisions to make is affected for evil by the results of improper diet. A disordered stomach produces a disordered, uncertain state of mind. Often it causes irritability, harshness, or injustice. Many a plan that would have been a blessing to the world has been set aside, many unjust, oppressive, even cruel measures have been carried, as the result of diseased conditions due to wrong habits of eating.

Here is a suggestion for all whose work is sedentary or chiefly mental; let those who have sufficient moral courage and self-control try it: At each meal take only two or three kinds of simple food, and eat no more than is required to satisfy hunger. Take active exercise every day, and see if you do not receive benefit.

Exercise Reason and Self-Control

Strong men who are engaged in active physical labor are not compelled to be as careful as to the quantity or quality of their food as are persons of sedentary habits; but even these would have better health if they would practice self-control in eating and drinking.

Some wish that an exact rule could be prescribed for their diet. They overeat, and then regret it, and so they keep thinking about what they eat and drink. This is not as it should be. One person cannot lay down an exact rule for another. Everyone should exercise reason and self-control and should act from principle.

Our bodies are Christ's purchased possession, and we are not at liberty to do with them as we please. All who understand the laws of health should realize their obligation to obey these laws which God has established in their being. Obedience to the laws of health is to be made a matter of personal duty. We ourselves must suffer the results of violated law. We must individually answer to God for our habits and practices. Therefore the question with us is not, "What is the world's practice?" but, "How shall I as an individual treat the habitation that God has given me?"

Choosing the Best Food

THE diet appointed man in the beginning did not include animal food. Not till after the Flood, when every green thing on the earth had been destroyed, did man receive permission to eat flesh.

In choosing man's food in Eden, the Lord showed what was the best diet; in the choice made for Israel He taught the same lesson. He brought the Israelites out of Egypt, and undertook their training, that they might be a people for His own possession. Through them He desired to bless and teach the world. He provided them with the food best adapted for this purpose, not flesh, but manna, "the bread of heaven." It was only because of their discontent and their murmuring for the fleshpots of Egypt that animal food was granted them, and this only for a short time. Its use brought disease and death to thousands. Yet the restriction to a non-flesh diet was never heartily accepted. It continued to be the cause of discontent and murmuring, open or secret, and it was not made permanent.

Upon their settlement in Canaan the Israelites were permitted the use of animal food, but under careful restrictions, which tended to lessen the evil results. The use of swine's flesh was prohibited, as also of other animals and of birds and fish whose flesh was pronounced unclean. Of the meats permitted, the eating of the fat and the blood was strictly forbidden.

Only such animals could be used for food as were in good condition. No creature that was torn, that had died of itself, or from which the blood had not been carefully drained, could be used as food.

By departing from the plan divinely appointed for their diet, the Israelites suffered great loss. They desired a flesh diet, and they reaped its results. They did not reach God's ideal of character or fulfill His purpose. The Lord "gave them their request; but sent leanness into their soul." Psalm 106:15. They valued the earthly above the spiritual, and the sacred preeminence which was His purpose for them they did not attain.

Those who eat flesh are but eating grains and vegetables at second hand; for the animal receives from these things the nutrition that produces growth. The life that was in the grains and vegetables passes into the eater. We receive it by eating the flesh of the animal. How much better to get it direct, by eating the food that God provided for our use!

Disease in Food Animals

Flesh was never the best food; but its use is now doubly objectionable, since disease in animals is so rapidly increasing. Those who use flesh foods little know what they are eating. Often if they could see the animals when living and know the quality of the meat they eat, they would turn from it with loathing. People are continually eating flesh that is filled with tuberculous and cancerous germs. Tu-

81

berculosis, cancer, and other fatal diseases are thus communicated.

The tissues of the swine swarm with parasites. Of the swine God said, "It is unclean unto you: ye shall not eat of their flesh, nor touch their dead carcass." Deuteronomy 14: 8. This command was given because swine's flesh is unfit for food. Swine are scavengers, and this is the only use they were intended to serve. Never, under any circumstances, was their flesh to be eaten by human beings. It is impossible for the flesh of any living creature to be wholesome when filth is its natural element, and when it feeds upon every detestable thing.

Often animals are taken to market, and sold for food, when they are so diseased that their owners fear to keep them longer. And some of the processes of fattening them for market produce disease. Shut away from the light and pure air, breathing the atmosphere of filthy stables, perhaps fattening on decaying food, the entire body soon becomes contaminated with foul matter.

Animals are often transported long distances and subjected to great suffering in reaching a market. Taken from the green pastures, and traveling for weary miles over the hot, dusty roads, or crowded into filthy cars, feverish and exhausted, often for many hours deprived of food and water, the poor creatures are driven to their death that human beings may feast on the carcasses.

In many places fish become so contaminated by the filth on which they feed as to be a cause of disease. This is especially the case where the fish come in contact with the sewage of large cities. The fish that are fed on the contents of the drains may pass into distant waters, and may be caught where the water is pure and fresh. Thus when used as food, they bring disease and death on those who do not suspect the danger.

Effects of a Meat Diet

The effects of a flesh diet may not be immediately realized, but this is no evidence that it is not harmful. Few can be made to believe that it is the meat they have eaten which has poisoned their blood and caused their suffering. Many die of diseases wholly due to meat eating, while the real cause is not suspected by themselves or by others.

The moral evils of a flesh diet are not less marked than are the physical ills. Flesh food is injurious to health, and whatever affects the body has a corresponding effect on the mind and the soul. Think of the cruelty to animals that meat eating involves, and its effect on those who inflict and those who behold it. How it destroys the tenderness with which we should regard these creatures of God!

The intelligence displayed by many dumb animals approaches so closely to human intelligence that it is a mystery. The animals see and hear and love and fear and suffer. They use their organs far more faithfully than many human beings use theirs. They manifest sympathy and tenderness toward their companions in suffering. Many animals show an affection for those who have charge of them, far superior to the affection shown by some of the human race. They form attachments for man which are not broken without great suffering to them.

What man with a human heart, who has ever cared for domestic animals, could look into their eyes, so full of confidence and affection, and willingly give them over to the butcher's knife? How could he devour their flesh as a sweet morsel?

It is a mistake to suppose that muscular strength depends on the use of animal food. The needs of the system can be better supplied, and more vigorous health can be enjoyed, without its use. The grains, with fruits, nuts, and vegetables, contain all the nutritive properties necessary to make good blood. These elements are not so well or so fully supplied by a flesh diet. Had the use of flesh been essential to health and strength, animal food would have been included in the diet appointed man in the beginning.

When the use of flesh food is discontinued, there is often a sense of weakness, a lack of vigor. Many urge this as evidence that flesh food is essential; but it is because foods of this class are stimulating, because they fever the blood and excite the nerves, that they are so missed. Some will find it as difficult to leave off flesh eating as it is for the drunkard to give up his dram, but they will be the better for the change.

A Variety of Foods

When flesh food is discarded, its place should be supplied with a variety of grains, nuts, vegetables, and fruits that will be both nourishing and appetizing. This is especially necessary in the case of those who are weak, or who are taxed with continuous labor. In some countries where poverty abounds flesh is the cheapest food. Under these circumstances the change will be made with greater difficulty; but it can be effected. We should, however, consider the situation of the people and the power of lifelong habit, and should be careful not to urge even right ideas unduly. None should be urged to make the change abruptly. The place of meat should be supplied with wholesome foods that are inexpensive. In this matter very much depends on the cook. With care and skill, dishes may be prepared that will be both nutritious and appetizing, and will, to a great degree, take the place of flesh food.

In all cases educate the conscience, enlist the will, supply good, wholesome food, and the change will be readily made, and the demand for flesh will soon cease.

Is it not time that all should aim to dispense with flesh foods? How can those who are seeking to become pure, refined, and holy, that they may have the companionship of heavenly angels, continue to use as food anything that has so harmful an effect on soul and body? How can they take the life of God's creatures that they may consume the flesh as a luxury? Let them, rather, return to the wholesome and delicious food given to man in the beginning, and themselves practice and teach their children to practice mercy toward the dumb creatures that God has made and has placed under our dominion.

A Balanced Diet

NOT all who profess to believe in dietetic reform are really reformers. With many persons the reform consists merely in discarding certain unwholesome foods. They do not understand clearly the principles of health, and their tables, still loaded with harmful dainties, are far from being an example of Christian temperance and moderation.

Another class, in their desire to set a right example, go to the opposite extreme. Some are unable to obtain the most desirable foods, and instead of using such things as would best supply the lack, they adopt an impoverished diet. Their food does not supply the elements needed to make good blood. Their health suffers, their usefulness is impaired, and their example tells against rather than in favor of reform in diet.

Others think that since health requires a simple diet, there need be little care in the selection or the preparation of food. Some restrict themselves to a very meager diet, not having sufficient variety to supply the needs of the system, and they suffer in consequence.

Those who have but a partial understanding of the principles of reform are often the most rigid, not only in carrying out their views themselves, but in urging them on their families and their neighbors. The effect of their mistaken reforms, as seen in their own ill health, and their efforts to force their views upon others, give many a false idea of dietetic reform, and lead them to reject it altogether.

Those who understand the laws of health and who are governed by principle will shun the extremes, both of indulgence and of restriction. Their diet is chosen, not for the mere gratification of appetite, but for the upbuilding of the body. They seek to preserve every power in the best condition for highest service to God and man. The appetite is under the control of reason and conscience, and they are rewarded with health of body and mind. While they do not urge their views offensively upon others, their example is a testimony in favor of right principles. These persons have a wide influence for good.

There is real common sense in dietetic reform. The subject should be studied broadly and deeply, and no one should criticize others because their practice is not, in all things, in harmony with his own. It is impossible to make an unvarying rule to regulate everyone's habits, and no one should think himself a criterion for all. Not all can eat the same things. Foods that are palatable and wholesome to one person may be distasteful, and even harmful, to another. Some cannot use milk, while others thrive on it. Some persons cannot digest peas and beans; others find them wholesome. For some the coarser grain preparations are good food, while others cannot use them.

The diet reform should be progressive. As disease in animals increases, the use of milk and eggs will become more and more unsafe. An effort should be made to supply their place with other things that are healthful and inexpensive.

87

The people everywhere should be taught how to cook without milk and eggs so far as possible, and yet have their food wholesome and palatable.

The practice of eating but two meals a day is generally found a benefit to health; yet under some circumstances persons may require a third meal. This should, however, if taken at all, be very light, and of food most easily digested. Crackers, the English biscuit, or zwieback, and fruit, or cereal coffee, are the foods best suited for the evening meal.

Relax While You Eat

Some are continually anxious lest their food, however simple and healthful, may hurt them. To these let me say, Do not think that your food will injure you; do not think about it at all. Eat according to your best judgment; and when you have asked the Lord to bless the food for the strengthening of your body, believe that He hears your prayer, and be at rest.

Because principle requires us to discard those things that irritate the stomach and impair health, we should remember that an impoverished diet produces poverty of the blood. Cases of disease most difficult to cure result from this cause. The system is not sufficiently nourished, and dyspepsia and general debility are the result. Those who use such a diet are not always compelled by poverty to do so, but they choose it through ignorance or negligence, or to carry out their erroneous ideas of reform.

God is not honored when the body is neglected or abused and is thus unfitted for His service. To care for the body by providing for it food that is relishable and strengthening is one of the first duties of the householder. It is far better to have less expensive clothing and furniture than to stint the supply of food.

Some householders stint the family table in order to provide expensive entertainment for visitors. This is unwise. In the entertainment of guests there should be greater simplicity. Let the needs of the family have first attention.

Unwise economy and artificial customs often prevent the exercise of hospitality where it is needed and would be a blessing. The regular supply of food for our tables should be such that the unexpected guest can be made welcome without burdening the housewife to make extra preparation.

All should learn what to eat and how to cook it. Men, as well as women, need to understand the simple, healthful preparation of food. Their business often calls them where they cannot obtain wholesome food; then, if they have a knowledge of cookery, they can use it to good purpose.

Carefully consider your diet. Study from cause to effect. Cultivate self-control. Keep appetite under the control of reason. Never abuse the stomach by overeating, but do not deprive yourself of the wholesome, palatable food that health demands.

Clothes for the Family

THE Bible teaches modesty in dress. "In like manner also, that women adorn themselves in modest apparel." 1 Timothy 2:9. This forbids display in dress, gaudy colors, profuse ornamentation. Any device designed to attract attention to the wearer or to excite admiration is excluded from the modest apparel which God's Word enjoins.

Our dress is to be inexpensive—not with "gold, or pearls, or costly array." 1 Timothy 2:9.

Money is a trust from God. It is not ours to expend for the gratification of pride or ambition. In the hands of God's children it is food for the hungry and clothing for the naked. It is a defense to the oppressed, a means of health to the sick, a means of preaching the gospel to the poor. You could bring happiness to many hearts by using wisely the means that is now spent for show. Consider the life of Christ. Study His character, and be partakers with Him in His self-denial.

In the professed Christian world enough is expended for jewels and needlessly expensive dress to feed all the hungry and to clothe the naked. Fashion and display absorb the means that might comfort the poor and the suffering. They rob the world of the gospel of the Saviour's love. Missions languish. Multitudes perish for want of Christian teaching. Beside our own doors and in foreign lands the heathen are untaught and unsaved.

Have a Heart!

While God has laden the earth with His bounties and filled its storehouses with the comforts of life, while He has so freely given to us a saving knowledge of His truth, what excuse can we offer for permitting the cries of the widow and the fatherless, the sick and the suffering, the untaught and the unsaved, to ascend to heaven? In the day of God, when brought face to face with Him who gave His life for these needy ones, what excuse will those offer who are spending their time and money upon indulgences that God has forbidden? To such will not Christ say, "I was anhungered, and ye gave Me no meat: I was thirsty, and ye gave Me no drink: . . . naked, and ye clothed Me not: sick, and in prison, and ye visited Me not"? Matthew 25:42, 43.

But our clothing, while modest and simple, should be of good quality, of becoming colors, and suited for service. It should be chosen for durability rather than display. It should provide warmth and proper protection. The wise woman described in the Proverbs "is not afraid of the snow for her household: for all her household are clothed with double garments." Proverbs 31:21, margin.

Our dress should be cleanly. Uncleanliness in dress is unhealthful, and thus defiling to the body and to the soul. "Ye are the temple of God. . . . If any man defile the temple of God, him shall God destroy." 1 Corinthians 3:16, 17.

In all respects the dress should be healthful. "Above all

things," God desires us to "be in health"—health of body and of soul. And we are to be workers together with Him for the health of both soul and body. Both are promoted by healthful dress.

It should have the grace, the beauty, the appropriateness of natural simplicity. Christ has warned us against the pride of life, but not against its grace and natural beauty. He pointed to the flowers of the field, to the lily unfolding in its purity, and said, "Even Solomon in all his glory was not arrayed like one of these." Matthew 6:29. Thus by the things of nature Christ illustrates the beauty that Heaven values, the modest grace, the simplicity, the purity, the appropriateness, that would make our attire pleasing to Him.

The most beautiful dress He bids us wear upon the soul. No outward adorning can compare in value or loveliness with that "meek and quiet spirit" which in His sight is "of great price." 1 Peter 3:4.

Words of Promise

To those who make the Saviour's principles their guide, how precious His words of promise:

"Why are ye anxious concerning raiment?" "If God doth so clothe the grass of the field, which today is, and tomorrow is cast into the oven, shall He not much more clothe you? . . . Be not therefore anxious, saying, . . . Wherewithal shall we be clothed? . . . For your heavenly Father knoweth that ye have need of all these things. But seek ye first His kingdom, and His righteousness; and all these things shall be added unto you." Matthew 6:28, 30-33, R.V.

"Thou wilt keep him in perfect peace, whose mind is stayed on Thee: because he trusteth in Thee." Isaiah 26:3.

What a contrast is this to the weariness, the unrest, the disease and wretchedness, that result from the rule of fashion! How contrary to the principles given in the Scriptures are many of the modes of dress that fashion prescribes! Think of the styles that have prevailed for the last few hundreds of years, or even for the last few decades. How many of them, when not in fashion, would be declared immodest; how many would be pronounced inappropriate for a refined, God-fearing, self-respecting woman.

The making of changes in apparel for the sake of fashion merely is not sanctioned by the Word of God. Changing styles and elaborate, costly ornamentation squander the time and means of the rich, and lay waste the energies of mind and soul. They impose a heavy burden on the middle and poorer classes.

Almost as soon as they come into the world the children are subjected to fashion's influence. They hear more of dress than of their Saviour. They see their mothers consulting the fashion plates more earnestly than the Bible. The display of dress is treated as of greater importance than the development of character. Parents and children are robbed of that which is best and sweetest and truest in life. For fashion's sake they are cheated out of a preparation for the life to come.

It was the adversary of all good who instigated the invention of the ever-changing fashions. He desires nothing so much as to bring grief and dishonor to God by working the misery and ruin of human beings. One of the means by which he most effectually accomplishes this is the devices of fashion, that weaken the body as well as enfeeble the mind and belittle the soul.

How Custom Affects Health

Women are subject to serious maladies, and their sufferings are greatly increased, by their manner of dress. Instead of preserving their health for the trying emergencies that are sure to come, they by their wrong habits too often sacrifice not only health but life, and leave to their children a legacy of woe in a ruined constitution, perverted habits, and false ideas of life.

One evil which custom fosters is the unequal distribution of the clothing, so that while some parts of the body have more than is required, others are insufficiently clad. The feet and limbs, being remote from the vital organs, should be especially guarded from cold by abundant clothing. It is impossible to have health when the extremities are habitually cold; for if there is too little blood in them there will be too much in other portions of the body. Perfect health requires a perfect circulation; but this cannot be had while three or four times as much clothing is worn upon the body, where the vital organs are situated, as upon the feet and limbs.

A multitude of women are nervous and careworn, because they deprive themselves of the pure air that would make pure blood, and of the freedom of motion that would send the blood bounding through the veins, giving life, health, and energy. Many women have become confirmed invalids when they might have enjoyed health, and many have died of consumption [tuberculosis] and other diseases when they might have lived their allotted term of life had

94

they dressed in accordance with health principles and exercised freely in the open air.

In order to secure the most healthful clothing, the needs of every part of the body must be carefully studied. The character of the climate, the surroundings, the condition of health, the age, and the occupation must all be considered. Every article of dress should fit easily, obstructing neither the circulation of the blood nor a free, full, natural respiration. Everything worn should be so loose that when the arms are raised the clothing will be correspondingly lifted.

Sensible Dress and Exercise

Women who are in failing health can do much for themselves by sensible dressing and exercise. When suitably dressed for outdoor enjoyment, let them exercise in the open air, carefully at first, but increasing the amount of exercise as they can endure it. By taking this course many might regain health and live to take their share in the world's work.

Let women themselves, instead of struggling to meet the demands of fashion, have the courage to dress healthfully and simply. Instead of sinking into a mere household drudge, let the wife and mother take time to read, to keep herself well informed, to be a companion to her husband, and to keep in touch with the developing minds of her children. Let her use wisely the opportunities now hers to influence her dear ones for the higher life. Let her take time to make the dear Saviour a daily companion and familiar friend. Let her take time for the study of His Word, take time to go with the children into the fields, and learn of God through the beauty of His works.

Stimulants and Narcotics

UNDER the head of stimulants and narcotics is classed a great variety of articles that, altogether used as food or drink, irritate the stomach, poison the blood, and excite the nerves. Their use is a positive evil. Men seek the excitement of stimulants, because, for the time, the results are agreeable. But there is always a reaction. The use of unnatural stimulants always tends to excess, and it is an active agent in promoting physical degeneration and decay.

In this fast age, the less exciting the food, the better. Condiments are injurious in their nature. Mustard, pepper, spices, pickles, and other things of a like character, irritate the stomach and make the blood feverish and impure. The inflamed condition of the drunkard's stomach is often pictured as illustrating the effect of alcoholic liquors. A similarly inflamed condition is produced by the use of irritating condiments. Soon ordinary food does not satisfy the appetite. The system feels a want, a craving, for something more stimulating.

Tea and Coffee

Tea acts as a stimulant, and, to a certain extent, produces intoxication. The action of coffee and many other popular drinks is similar. The first effect is exhilarating. The nerves of the stomach are excited; these convey irritation to the brain, and this in turn is aroused to impart increased action to the heart and short-lived energy to the entire system. Fatigue is forgotten, the strength seems to be increased. The intellect is aroused, the imagination becomes more vivid.

Because of these results many suppose that their tea or coffee is doing them great good. But this is a mistake. Tea and coffee do not nourish the system. Their effect is produced before there has been time for digestion and assimilation, and what seems to be strength is only nervous excitement. When the influence of the stimulant is gone the unnatural force abates, and the result is a corresponding degree of languor and debility.

The continued use of these nerve irritants is followed by headache, wakefulness, palpitation of the heart, indigestion, trembling, and many other evils; for they wear away the life forces. Tired nerves need rest and quiet instead of stimulation and overwork. Nature needs time to recuperate her exhausted energies. When her forces are goaded on by the use of stimulants, more will be accomplished for a time; but, as the system becomes debilitated by their constant use, it gradually becomes more difficult to rouse the energies to the desired point. The demand for stimulants becomes more difficult to control, until the will is overborne, and there seems to be no power to deny the unnatural craving. Stronger and still stronger stimulants are called for, until exhausted nature can no longer respond.

Tobacco a Slow Poison

Tobacco is a slow, insidious, but most malignant poison. In whatever form it is used, it tells upon the constitution;

97

it is all the more dangerous because its effects are slow, and at first hardly perceptible. It excites and then paralyzes the nerves. It weakens and clouds the brain. Often it affects the nerves in a more powerful manner than does intoxicating drink. It is more subtle, and its effects are difficult to eradicate from the system. Its use excites a thirst for strong drink, and in many cases lays the foundation for the liquor habit.

The use of tobacco is inconvenient, expensive, uncleanly, defiling to the user, and offensive to others. Its devotees are encountered everywhere. You rarely pass through a crowd but some smoker puffs his poisoned breath in your face. It is unpleasant and unhealthful to remain in a railway car or in a room where the atmosphere is laden with the fumes of liquor and tobacco. Though men persist in using these poisons themselves, what right have they to defile the air that others must breathe?

Why Do Boys Smoke?

Among children and youth the use of tobacco is working untold harm. The unhealthful practices of past generations affect the children and youth of today. Mental inability, physical weakness, disordered nerves, and unnatural cravings are transmitted as a legacy from parents to children. And the same practices, continued by the children, are increasing and perpetuating the evil results. To this cause in no small degree is owing the physical, mental, and moral deterioration which is becoming such a cause of alarm.

Boys begin the use of tobacco at a very early age. The habit thus formed, when body and mind are especially susceptible to its effects, undermines the physical strength, dwarfs the body, stupefies the mind, and corrupts the morals.

But what can be done to teach children and youth the evils of a practice of which parents, teachers, and ministers set them the example? Little boys, hardly emerged from babyhood, may be seen smoking their cigarettes. If one speaks to them about it, they say, "My father uses tobacco." They point to the minister or the Sunday school superintendent, and say, "Such a man smokes; what harm for me to do as he does?" Many workers in the temperance cause are addicted to the use of tobacco. What power can such persons have to stay the progress of intemperance?

I appeal to those who profess to believe and obey the Word of God: Can you as Christians indulge a habit that is paralyzing your intellect, and robbing you of power rightly to estimate eternal realities? Can you consent daily to rob God of service which is His due, and to rob your fellowmen both of service you might render and of the power of example?

Have you considered your responsibility as God's stewards for the means in your hands? How much of the Lord's money do you spend for tobacco? Reckon up what you have thus spent during your lifetime. How does the amount consumed by this defiling lust compare with what you have given for the relief of the poor and the spread of the gospel?

The Victim of Intoxicating Drink

"Know ye not that . . . ye are not your own? For ye are bought with a price: therefore glorify God in your body, and in your spirit, which are God's." 1 Corinthians 6:19, 20.

99

"Wine is a mocker, strong drink is raging:
And whosoever is deceived thereby is not wise."
"Who hath woe? who hath sorrow? who hath contentions?
who hath babbling? who hath wounds without cause?
Who hath redness of eyes?
They that tarry long at the wine;
They that go to seek mixed wine.
Look not thou upon the wine when it is red,
When it giveth his color in the cup,
When it moveth itself aright.
At the last it biteth like a serpent,
And stingeth like an adder." Proverbs 20:1; 23:29-32.

Never was traced by human hand a more vivid picture of the debasement and the slavery of the victim of intoxicating drink. Enthralled, degraded, even when awakened to a sense of his misery he has no power to break from the snare; he "will seek it yet again." Proverbs 23:35.

No argument is needed to show the evil effects of intoxicants on the drunkard. The bleared, besotted wrecks of humanity—souls for whom Christ died, and over whom angels weep—are everywhere. They are a blot on our boasted civilization. They are the shame and curse and peril of every land.

And who can picture the wretchedness, the agony, the despair, that are hidden in the drunkard's home? Think of the wife, often delicately reared, sensitive, cultured, and refined, linked to one whom drink transforms into a sot or a demon. Think of the children, robbed of home comforts, education, and training, living in terror of him who should be their pride and protection, thrust into the world, bearing the brand of shame, often with the hereditary curse of the drunkard's thirst.

100

The Cause of Many Accidents

Think of the frightful accidents that are every day occurring through the influence of drink. Some official on a railway train neglects to heed a signal, or misinterprets an order. On goes the train; there is a collision, and many lives are lost. Or a steamer is run aground, and passengers and crew find a watery grave. When the matter is investigated, it is found that someone at an important post was under the influence of drink. To what extent can one indulge the liquor habit and be safely trusted with the lives of human beings? He can be trusted only as he totally abstains.

Intoxication is just as really produced by wine, beer, and cider as by stronger drinks. The use of these drinks awakens the taste for those that are stronger, and thus the liquor habit is established. Moderate drinking is the school in which men are educated for the drunkard's career. Yet so insidious is the work of these milder stimulants that the highway to drunkenness is entered before the victim suspects his danger.

Some who are never considered really drunk are always under the influence of mild intoxicants. They are feverish, unstable in mind, unbalanced. Imagining themselves secure, they go on and on until every barrier is broken down, every principle sacrificed. The strongest resolutions are undermined, the highest considerations are not sufficient to keep the debased appetite under the control of reason.

The Wine of Cana

The Bible nowhere sanctions the use of intoxicating wine. The wine that Christ made from water at the marriage feast of Cana was the pure juice of the grape. This is "the new wine . . . found in the cluster," of which the Scripture says, "Destroy it not; for a blessing is in it." Isaiah 65:8.

It was Christ who, in the Old Testament, gave the warning to Israel, "Wine is a mocker, strong drink is raging: and whosoever is deceived thereby is not wise." Proverbs 20:1. He Himself provided no such beverage. Satan tempts men to indulgence that will becloud reason and benumb the spiritual perceptions, but Christ teaches us to bring the lower nature into subjection. He never places before men that which would be a temptation. His whole life was an example of self-denial. It was to break the power of appetite that in the forty days' fast in the wilderness He suffered in our behalf the severest test that humanity could endure. It was Christ who directed that John the Baptist should drink neither wine nor strong drink. It was He who enjoined similar abstinence upon the wife of Manoah. Christ did not contradict His own teaching. The unfermented wine that He provided for the wedding guests was a wholesome and refreshing drink. This is the wine that was used by our Saviour and His disciples in the first Communion. It is the wine that should always be used on the Communion table as a symbol of the Saviour's blood. The sacramental service is designed to be soul-refreshing and lifegiving. There is to be connected with it nothing that could minister to evil.

Often intemperance begins in the home. By the use of rich, unhealthful food the digestive organs are weakened, and a desire is created for food that is still more stimulating. Thus the appetite is educated to crave continually some-

102

thing stronger. The demand for stimulants becomes more frequent and more difficult to resist. The system becomes more or less filled with poison, and the more debilitated it becomes, the greater is the desire for these things. One step in the wrong direction prepares the way for another. Many who would not be guilty of placing on their table wine or liquor of any kind will load their table with food which creates such a thirst for strong drink that to resist the temptation is almost impossible. Wrong habits of eating and drinking destroy the health and prepare the way for drunkenness.

Educate the Appetite

There is work for mothers in helping their children to form correct habits and pure tastes. Educate the appetite; teach the children to abhor stimulants. Bring your children up to have moral stamina to resist the evil that surrounds them. Teach them that they are not to be swayed by others, that they are not to yield to strong influences, but to influence others for good.

Great efforts are made to put down intemperance, but there is much effort that is not directed to the right point. The advocates of temperance reform should be awake to the evils resulting from the use of unwholesome food, condiments, tea, and coffee.

It must be kept before the people that the right balance of the mental and moral powers depends in a great degree on the right condition of the physical system. All narcotics and unnatural stimulants that enfeeble and degrade the physical nature tend to lower the tone of the intellect and morals. Intemperance lies at the foundation of the moral depravity of the world. By the indulgence of perverted appetite, man loses his power to resist temptation.

In relation to tea, coffee, tobacco, and alcoholic drinks, the only safe course is to touch not, taste not, handle not. The tendency of tea, coffee, and similar drinks is in the same direction as that of alcoholic liquor and tobacco, and in some cases the habit is as difficult to break as it is for the drunkard to give up intoxicants. Those who attempt to leave off these stimulants will for a time feel a loss, and will suffer without them. But by persistence they will overcome the craving and cease to feel the lack. Nature may require a little time to recover from the abuse she has suffered; but give her a chance, and she will again rally, and perform her work nobly and well.

Liquor and Modern Life

"WOE unto him that buildeth his house by unrighteousness, and his chambers by wrong; . . . that saith, I will build me a wide house and large chambers, and cutteth him out windows; and it is ceiled with cedar, and painted with vermilion. Shalt thou reign, because thou closest thyself in cedar? . . . Thine eyes and thine heart are not but for thy covetousness, and for to shed innocent blood, and for oppression, and for violence, to do it." Jeremiah 22:13-17.

This scripture pictures the work of those who manufacture and who sell intoxicating liquor. Their business means robbery. For the money they receive no equivalent is returned. Every dollar they add to their gains has brought a curse to the spender.

With a liberal hand, God has bestowed His blessings upon men. If His gifts were wisely used, how little the world would know of poverty or distress! It is the wickedness of men that turns His blessings into a curse. It is through the greed of gain and the lust of appetite that the grains and fruits given for our sustenance are converted into poisons that bring misery and ruin.

Every year millions upon millions of gallons of intoxicating liquors are consumed. Millions upon millions of dollars are spent in buying wretchedness, poverty, disease, degradation, lust, crime, and death. For the sake of gain, the liquor seller deals out to his victims that which corrupts and destroys mind and body. He entails on the drunkard's family poverty and wretchedness.

Houses of prostitution, dens of vice, criminal courts, prisons, almshouses, insane asylums, hospitals—all are, to a great degree, filled as a result of the liquor seller's work. Like the mystic Babylon of the Apocalypse, he is dealing in "slaves, and souls of men." Behind the liquor seller stands the mighty destroyer of souls, and every art which earth or hell can devise is employed to draw human beings under his power. In the city and the country, on the railway trains, on the great steamers, in places of business, in the halls of pleasure, in the medical dispensary, even in the church on the sacred Communion table, his traps are set. Nothing is left undone to create and to foster the desire for intoxicants.

Day by day, month by month, year by year, the work goes on. Fathers and husbands and brothers, the stay and hope and pride of the nation, are steadily passing into the liquor dealer's haunts, to be sent back wrecked and ruined.

The Shadow of Drinking Parents

More terrible still, the curse is striking the very heart of the home. More and more, women are forming the liquor habit. In many a household, little children, even in the innocence and helplessness of babyhood, are in daily peril through the neglect, the abuse, the vileness of drunken mothers. Sons and daughters are growing up under the shadow of this terrible evil. What outlook for their future but that they will sink even lower than their parents?

From so-called Christian lands the curse is carried to the

regions of idolatry. The poor, ignorant savages are taught the use of liquor. Even among the heathen, men of intelligence recognize and protest against it as a deadly poison; but in vain have they sought to protect their lands from its ravages. By civilized peoples, tobacco, liquor, and opium are forced upon the heathen nations. The ungoverned passions of the savage, stimulated by drink, drag him down to degradation before unknown, and it becomes an almost hopeless undertaking to send missionaries to these lands.

Through their contact with peoples who should have given them a knowledge of God, the heathen are led into vices which are proving the destruction of whole tribes and races. And in the dark places of the earth the men of civilized nations are hated because of this.

Money Stained With Blood

The liquor interest is a power in the world. It has on its side the combined strength of money, habit, appetite. Its power is felt even in the church. Men whose money has been made, directly or indirectly, in the liquor traffic, are members of churches, "in good and regular standing." Many of them give liberally to popular charities. Their contributions help to support the enterprises of the church and to sustain its ministers. They command the consideration shown to the money power. Churches that accept such members are virtually sustaining the liquor traffic. Too often the minister has not the courage to stand for the right. He does not declare to his people what God has said concerning the work of the liquor seller. To speak plainly would mean the offending of his congregation, the sacrifice of his popularity, the loss of his salary.

But above the tribunal of the church is the tribunal of God. He who declared to the first murderer, "The voice of thy brother's blood crieth unto Me from the ground" (Genesis 4:10), will not accept for His altar the gifts of the liquor dealer. His anger is kindled against those who attempt to cover their guilt with a cloak of liberality. Their money is stained with blood. A curse is upon it. Isaiah 1:11-15.

The drunkard is capable of better things. He has been entrusted with talents with which to honor God and bless the world; but his fellowmen have laid a snare for his soul, and built themselves up by his degradation. They have lived in luxury, while the poor victims whom they have robbed lived in poverty and wretchedness. But God will require for this at the hand of him who has helped to speed the drunkard on to ruin. He who rules in the heavens has not lost sight of the first cause or the last effect of drunkenness. He who has a care for the sparrow and clothes the grass of the field will not pass by those who have been formed in His own image, purchased with His own blood, and pay no heed to their cries. God marks all this wickedness that perpetuates crime and misery.

Woes on the Liquor Seller

The world and the church may have approval for the man who has gained wealth by degrading the human soul. They may smile upon him by whom men are led down step by step in the path of shame and degradation. But God notes it all, and renders a just judgment. The liquor seller may be termed by the world a good businessman; but the Lord says, "Woe unto him." He will be charged with the hopelessness, the misery, the suffering, brought into the world by the liquor traffic. He will have to answer for the want and woe of the mothers and children who have suffered for food and clothing and shelter, and who have buried all hope and joy. He will have to answer for the souls he has sent unprepared into eternity. And those who sustain the liquor seller in his work are sharers in his guilt. To them God says, "Your hands are full of blood."

The licensing of the liquor traffic is advocated by many as tending to restrict the drink evil. But the licensing of the traffic places it under the protection of law. The government sanctions its existence, and thus fosters the evil which it professes to restrict. Under the protection of license laws, breweries, distilleries, and wineries are planted all over the land, and the liquor seller plies his work beside our very doors.

Often he is forbidden to sell intoxicants to one who is drunk or who is known to be a confirmed drunkard; but the work of making drunkards of the youth goes steadily forward. Upon the creating of the liquor appetite in the youth the very life of the traffic depends. The youth are led on, step by step, until the liquor habit is established, and the thirst is created that at any cost demands satisfaction. Less harmful would it be to grant liquor to the confirmed drunkard, whose ruin, in most cases, is already determined, than to permit the flower of our youth to be lured to destruction through this terrible habit.

By the licensing of the liquor traffic, temptation is kept constantly before those who are trying to reform. Institutions have been established where the victims of intemperance may be helped to overcome their appetite. This is a noble work; but so long as the sale of liquor is sanctioned by law, the intemperate receive little benefit. The appetite for intoxicating drink, though subdued, is not wholly destroyed; and when temptation assails them, as it does on every hand, they too often fall an easy prey.

The man who has a vicious beast, and who, knowing its disposition, allows it liberty, is by the laws of the land held accountable for the evil the beast may do. In the laws given to Israel the Lord directed that when a beast known to be vicious caused the death of a human being, the life of the owner should pay the price of his carelessness or malignity. On the same principle the government that licenses the liquor seller should be held responsible for the results of his traffic. And if it is a crime worthy of death to give liberty to a vicious beast, how much greater is the crime of sanctioning the work of the liquor seller!

Huge Financial Losses

Licenses are granted on the plea that they bring a revenue to the public treasury. But what is this revenue when compared with the enormous expense incurred for the criminals, the insane, the paupers, that are the fruit of the liquor traffic! A man under the influence of liquor commits a crime; he is brought into court, and those who legalized the traffic are forced to deal with the result of their own work. They authorized the sale of a draft that would make a sane man mad; and now it is necessary for them to send the man to prison or to the gallows, while often his wife and children are left destitute, to become the charge of the community in which they live.

Considering only the financial aspect of the question, what folly it is to tolerate such a business! But what revenue

110

can compensate for the loss of human reason, for the defacing and deforming of the image of God in man, for the ruin of children, reduced to pauperism and degradation, to perpetuate in their children the evil tendencies of their drunken fathers?

The man who has formed the habit of using intoxicants is in a desperate situation. His brain is diseased, his willpower is weakened. So far as any power in himself is concerned, his appetite is uncontrollable. He cannot be reasoned with or persuaded to deny himself. Drawn into the dens of vice, one who has resolved to quit drink is led to seize the glass again, and with the first taste of the intoxicant every good resolution is overpowered, every vestige of will destroyed. One taste of the maddening draft, and all thought of its results has vanished. The heartbroken wife is forgotten. The debauched father no longer cares that his children are hungry and naked. By legalizing the traffic, the law gives its sanction to this downfall of the soul and refuses to stop the trade that fills the world with evil.

There is no man whose interests the liquor traffic does not imperil. There is no man who for his own safeguard should not set himself to destroy it.

Above all other places having to do with secular interests only, legislative halls and courts of justice should be free from the curse of intemperance. Governors, senators, representatives, judges, men who enact and administer a nation's laws, men who hold in their hands the lives, the fair fame, the possessions of their fellows, should be men of strict temperance. Only thus can their minds be clear to discriminate between right and wrong. Only thus can they possess firmness of principle, and wisdom to administer

111

justice and to show mercy. But how does the record stand? How many of these men have their minds beclouded, their sense of right and wrong confused, by strong drink!

The honor of God, the stability of the nation, the well-being of the community, of the home, and of the individual, demand that every possible effort be made in arousing the people to the evil of intemperance. Soon we shall see the result of this terrible evil as we do not see it now. Who will put forth a determined effort to stay the work of destruction? As yet the contest has hardly begun. Let an army be formed to stop the sale of the drugged liquors that are making men mad. Let the danger from the liquor traffic be made plain, and a public sentiment be created that shall demand its prohibition. Let the drink-maddened men be given an opportunity to escape from their thralldom. Let the voice of the nation demand of its lawmakers that a stop be put to this infamous traffic.

Intemperance Can Be Cured

AMONG the victims of intemperance are men of all classes and all professions. Men of high station, of eminent talents, of great attainments, have yielded to the indulgence of appetite, until they are helpless to resist temptation. Some of them who were once in the possession of wealth are without home, without friends, in suffering, misery, disease, and degradation. They have lost their self-control. Unless a helping hand is held out to them, they will sink lower and lower. With these, self-indulgence is not only a moral sin, but a physical disease.

Often in helping the intemperate we must, as Christ so often did, give first attention to their physical condition. They need wholesome, unstimulating food and drink, clean clothing, opportunity to secure physical cleanliness. They need to be surrounded with an atmosphere of helpful, uplifting Christian influence. In every city a place should be provided where the slaves of evil habit may receive help to break the chains that bind them. Strong drink is regarded by many as the only solace in trouble; but this need not be if, instead of acting the part of the priest and Levite, professed Christians would follow the example of the Good Samaritan.

As the drunkard awakens to a sense of his degradation, do all in your power to show that you are his friend. Speak no word of censure. Let no act or look express reproach or aversion. Very likely the poor soul curses himself. Help him to rise. Speak words that will encourage faith. Seek to strengthen every good trait in his character. Teach him how to reach upward. Show him that it is possible for him to live so as to win the respect of his fellowmen. Help him to see the value of the talents which God has given him, but which he has neglected to improve.

Hope in Christ

Although the will has been depraved and weakened, there is hope for him in Christ. He will awaken in the heart higher impulses and holier desires. Encourage him to lay hold of the hope set before him in the gospel. Open the Bible before the tempted, struggling one, and over and over again read to him the promises of God. These promises will be to him as the leaves of the tree of life. Patiently continue your efforts until with grateful joy the trembling hand grasps the hope of redemption through Christ.

You must hold fast to those whom you are trying to help, else victory will never be yours. They will be continually tempted to evil. Again and again they will be almost overcome by the craving for strong drink; again and again they may fall; but do not, because of this, cease your efforts.

They have decided to make an effort to live for Christ; but their willpower is weakened, and they must be carefully guarded by those who watch for souls as they that must give an account. They have lost their manhood, and this they must win back. Many have to battle against strong hereditary tendencies to evil. Unnatural cravings, sensual impulses, were their inheritance from birth. These must be carefully guarded against. Within and without, good and evil are striving for the mastery. Those who have never passed through such experiences cannot know the almost overmastering power of appetite, or the fierceness of the conflict between habits of self-indulgence and the determination to be temperate in all things. Over and over again the battle must be fought.

Many who are drawn to Christ will not have moral courage to continue the warfare against appetite and passion. But the worker must not be discouraged by this. Is it only those rescued from the lowest depths that backslide?

Remember that you do not work alone. Ministering angels unite in service with every truehearted son and daughter of God. And Christ is the restorer. The Great Physician Himself stands beside His faithful workers, saying to the repentant soul, "Child, thy sins are forgiven." Mark 2:5, R.V., margin.

Many are the outcasts who will grasp the hope set before them in the gospel, and will enter the kingdom of heaven, while others who were blessed with great opportunities and great light which they did not improve will be left in outer darkness.

Necessity of Self-Effort

The victims of evil habit must be aroused to the necessity of making an effort for themselves. Others may put forth the most earnest endeavor to uplift them, the grace of God may be freely offered. Christ may entreat, His angels

115

may minister; but all will be in vain unless they themselves are roused to fight the battle in their own behalf.

The last words of David to Solomon, then a young man, and soon to receive the crown of Israel, were, "Be thou strong therefore, and show thyself a man." 1 Kings 2:2. To every child of humanity, the candidate for an immortal crown, are these words of inspiration spoken. "Be thou strong therefore, and show thyself a man."

The self-indulgent must be led to see and feel that great moral renovation is necessary if they would be men. God calls upon them to arouse, and in the strength of Christ win back the God-given manhood that has been sacrificed through sinful indulgence.

Feeling the terrible power of temptation, the drawing of desire that leads to indulgence, many a man cries in despair, "I cannot resist evil." Tell him that he can, that he must resist. He may have been overcome again and again, but it need not be always thus. He is weak in moral power, controlled by the habits of a life of sin. His promises and resolutions are like ropes of sand. The knowledge of his broken promises and forfeited pledges weakens his confidence in his own sincerity, and causes him to feel that God cannot accept him or work with his efforts. But he need not despair.

True Force of the Will

Those who put their trust in Christ are not to be enslaved by any hereditary or cultivated habit or tendency. Instead of being held in bondage to the lower nature, they are to rule every appetite and passion. God has not left us to battle with evil in our own finite strength. Whatever may be our inherited or cultivated tendencies to wrong, we

116

can overcome through the power that He is ready to impart.

The tempted one needs to understand the true force of the will. This is the governing power in the nature of man —the power of decision, of choice. Everything depends on the right action of the will. Desires for goodness and purity are right, so far as they go; but if we stop here, they avail nothing. Many will go down to ruin while hoping and desiring to overcome their evil propensities. They do not yield the will to God. They do not *choose* to serve Him.

God has given us the power of choice; it is ours to exercise. We cannot change our hearts; we cannot control our thoughts, our impulses, our affections. We cannot make ourselves pure, fit for God's service. But we can *choose* to serve God, we can give Him our will; then He will work in us to will and to do according to His good pleasure. Thus our whole nature will be brought under the control of Christ.

Through the right exercise of the will an entire change may be made in the life. By yielding up the will to Christ, we ally ourselves with divine power. We receive strength from above to hold us steadfast. A pure and noble life, a life of victory over appetite and lust, is possible to everyone who will unite his weak, wavering human will to the omnipotent, unwavering will of God.

Those who are struggling against the power of appetite should be instructed in the principles of healthful living. They should be shown that violation of the laws of health, by creating diseased conditions and unnatural cravings, lays the foundation of the liquor habit. Only by living in obedience to the principles of health can they hope to be freed from the craving for unnatural stimulants. While they depend upon divine strength to break the bonds of appetite, they are to cooperate with God by obedience to His laws, both moral and physical. Those who are endeavoring to reform should be provided with employment.

Those who work for the fallen will be disappointed in many who give promise of reform. Many will make but a superficial change in their habits and practices. They are moved by impulse, and for a time may seem to have reformed; but there is no real change of heart. They cherish the same self-love, have the same hungering for foolish pleasures, the same desire for self-indulgence. They have not a knowledge of the work of character building, and they cannot be relied upon as men of principle. They have debased their mental and spiritual powers by the gratification of appetite and passion, and this makes them weak. They are fickle and changeable. Their impulses tend toward sensuality. These persons are often a source of danger to others. Being looked upon as reformed men and women, they are trusted with responsibilities, and are placed where their influence corrupts the innocent.

The Danger of Falling

Even those who are sincerely seeking to reform are not beyond the danger of falling. They need to be treated with great wisdom as well as tenderness. The disposition to flatter and exalt those who have been rescued from the lowest depths sometimes proves their ruin. The practice of inviting men and women to relate in public the experience of their life of sin is full of danger to both speaker and hearers. To dwell upon scenes of evil is corrupting to mind and

118

soul. And the prominence given to the rescued ones is harmful to them. Many are led to feel that their sinful life has given them a certain distinction. A love of notoriety and a spirit of self-trust are encouraged that prove fatal to the soul. Only in distrust of self and dependence on the mercy of Christ can they stand.

All who give evidence of true conversion should be encouraged to work for others. Let none turn away a soul who leaves the service of Satan for the service of Christ. When one gives evidence that the Spirit of God is striving with him, present every encouragement for entering the Lord's service. "Of some have compassion, making a difference." Jude 22. Those who are wise in the wisdom that comes from God will see souls in need of help, those who have sincerely repented, but who without enouragement would hardly dare to lay hold of hope. The Lord will put it into the hearts of His servants to welcome these trembling, repentant ones to their loving fellowship. Whatever may have been their besetting sins, however low they may have fallen, when in contrition they come to Christ, He receives them. Then give them something to do for Him. If they desire to labor in uplifting others from the pit of destruction from which they themselves were rescued, give them opportunity. Bring them into association with experienced Christians, that they may gain spiritual strength. Fill their hearts and hands with work for the Master.

Through Faith in Christ

When light flashes into the soul, some who appeared to be most fully given to sin will become successful workers for just such sinners as they themselves once were. Through faith in Christ, some will rise to high places of service, and be entrusted with responsibilities in the work of saving souls. They see where their own weakness lies, they realize the depravity of their nature. They know the strength of sin, the power of evil habit. They realize their inability to overcome without the help of Christ, and their constant cry is, "I cast my helpless soul on Thee."

These can help others. The one who has been tempted and tried, whose hope was well-nigh gone, but who was saved by hearing a message of love, can understand the science of soul saving. He whose heart is filled with love for Christ because he himself has been sought for by the Saviour, and brought back to the fold, knows how to seek the lost. He can point sinners to the Lamb of God. He has given himself without reserve to God, and has been accepted in the Beloved. The hand that in weakness was held out for help has been grasped. By the ministry of such ones, many prodigals will be brought to the Father.

Remedy for Sin

For every soul struggling to rise from a life of sin to a life of purity, the great element of power abides in the only "name under heaven given among men, whereby we must be saved." Acts 4:12. "If any man thirst," for restful hope, for deliverance from sinful propensities, Christ says, "let him come unto Me, and drink." John 7:37. The only remedy for vice is the grace and power of Christ.

The good resolutions made in one's own strength avail nothing. Not all the pledges in the world will break the power of evil habit. Never will men practice temperance in all things until their hearts are renewed by divine grace.

We cannot keep ourselves from sin for one moment. Every moment we are dependent upon God.

True reformation begins with soul cleansing. Our work for the fallen will achieve real success only as the grace of Christ reshapes the character and the soul is brought into living connection with God.

Christ lived a life of perfect obedience to God's law, and in this He set an example for every human being. The life that He lived in this world we are to live, through His power and under His instruction.

In our work for the fallen, the claims of the law of God and the need of loyalty to Him are to be impressed on mind and heart. Never fail to show that there is a marked difference between the one who serves God and the one who serves Him not. God is love, but He cannot excuse willful disregard for His commands. The enactments of His government are such that men do not escape the consequences of disloyalty. Only those who honor Him can He honor. Man's conduct in this world decides his eternal destiny. As he has sown, so he must reap. Cause will be followed by effect.

Nothing less than perfect obedience can meet the standard of God's requirement. He has not left His requirements indefinite. He has enjoined nothing that is not necessary in order to bring man into harmony with Him.

The Saviour took upon Himself the infirmities of humanity and lived a sinless life that men might have no fear that because of the weakness of human nature they could not overcome. Christ came to make us "partakers of the divine nature," and His life declares that humanity, combined with divinity, does not commit sin.

121

The Saviour overcame to show man how he may overcome. All the temptations of Satan, Christ met with the Word of God. By trusting in God's promises, He received power to obey God's commandments, and the tempter could gain no advantage. To every temptation His answer was, "It is written." So God has given us His Word wherewith to resist evil. "Exceeding great and precious promises" are ours, that by these we "might be partakers of the divine nature, having escaped the corruption that is in the world through lust." 2 Peter 1:4.

Bid the tempted one look not to circumstances, to the weakness of self, or to the power of temptation, but to the power of God's Word. All its strength is ours. "Thy Word," says the psalmist, "have I hid in mine heart, that I might not sin against Thee." "By the word of Thy lips I have kept me from the paths of the destroyer." Psalms 119:11; 17:4.

Talk courage to the people; lift them up to God in prayer. Many who have been overcome by temptation are humiliated by their failures, and they feel that it is in vain for them to approach unto God; but this thought is of the enemy's suggestion. When they have sinned, and feel that they cannot pray, tell them that it is then the time to pray. Ashamed they may be, and deeply humbled; but as they confess their sins, He who is faithful and just will forgive their sins, and cleanse them from all unrighteousness.

Nothing is apparently more helpless, yet really more invincible, than the soul that feels its nothingness and relies wholly on the merits of the Saviour. By prayer, by the study of His Word, by faith in His abiding presence, the weakest of human beings may live in contact with the living Christ, and He will hold them by a hand that will never let go.

The Road to Health

THROUGH the agencies of nature, God is working, day by day, hour by hour, moment by moment, to keep us alive, to build up and restore us. When any part of the body sustains injury, a healing process is at once begun; nature's agencies are set at work to restore soundness. But the power working through these agencies is the power of God. All life-giving power is from Him. When one recovers from disease, it is God who restores him.

Sickness, suffering, and death are work of an antagonistic power. Satan is the destroyer; God is the restorer.

The words spoken to Israel are true today of those who recover health of body or health of soul. "I am the Lord that healeth thee." Exodus 15:26.

The desire of God for every human being is expressed in the words, "Beloved, I wish above all things that thou mayest prosper and be in health, even as thy soul prospereth." 3 John 2.

He it is "who forgiveth all thine iniquities; who healeth all thy diseases; who redeemeth thy life from destruction; who crowneth thee with loving-kindness and tender mercies." Psalm 103:3, 4.

123

When Christ healed disease, He warned many of the afflicted ones, "Sin no more, lest a worse thing come unto thee." John 5:14. Thus He taught that they had brought disease upon themselves by transgressing the laws of God, and that health could be preserved only by obedience.

Obedience the Way of Life

Let it be made plain that the way of God's commandments is the way of life. God has established the laws of nature, but His laws are not arbitrary exactions. Every "Thou shalt not," whether in physical or in moral law, implies a promise. If we obey it, blessing will attend our steps. God never forces us to do right, but He seeks to save us from the evil and lead us to the good.

Let attention be called to the laws that were taught to Israel. God gave them definite instruction in regard to their habits of life. He made known to them the laws relating to both physical and spiritual well-being; and on condition of obedience He assured them, "The Lord will take away from thee all sickness." Deuteronomy 7:15.

"Set your hearts unto all the words which I testify among you this day." "For they are life unto those that find them, and health to all their flesh." Deuteronomy 32:46; Proverbs 4:22.

God desires us to reach the standard of perfection made possible for us by the gift of Christ. He calls upon us to make our choice on the right side, to connect with heavenly agencies, to adopt principles that will restore in us the divine image. In His Written Word and in the great book of nature He has revealed the principles of life. It is our work to obtain a knowledge of these principles, and by obedience to cooperate with Him in restoring health to the body as well as to the soul.

Men need to learn that the blessings of obedience, in their fullness, can be theirs only as they receive the grace of Christ. It is His grace that gives man power to obey the laws of God. It is this that enables him to break the bondage of evil habit. This is the only power that can make him and keep him steadfast in the right path.

Vitalizing Power of Love

When the gospel is received in its purity and power, it is a cure for the maladies that originated in sin. The Sun of Righteousness arises, "with healing in His wings." Malachi 4:2. Not all that this world bestows can heal a broken heart, or impart peace of mind, or remove care, or banish disease. Fame, genius, talent—all are powerless to gladden the sorrowful heart or to restore the wasted life. The life of God in the soul is man's only hope.

The love which Christ diffuses through the whole being is a vitalizing power. Every vital part—the brain, the heart, the nerves—it touches with healing. By it the highest energies of the being are roused to activity. It frees the soul from the guilt and sorrow, the anxiety and care, that crush the life forces. With it come serenity and composure. It implants in the soul joy that nothing earthly can destroy—joy in the Holy Spirit—health-giving, life-giving joy.

Our Saviour's words, "Come unto Me, . . . and I will give you rest" (Matthew 11:28), are a prescription for the healing of physical, mental, and spiritual ills. Though men have brought suffering upon themselves by their own wrongdoing, He regards them with pity. In Him they may find help. He will do great things for those who trust in Him.

Although for ages sin has been strengthening its hold on the human race, although through falsehood and artifice Satan has cast the black shadow of his interpretation upon the Word of God, and has caused men to doubt His goodness; yet the Father's mercy and love have not ceased to flow earthward in rich currents. If human beings would open the windows of the soul heavenward in appreciation of the divine gifts, a flood of healing virtue would pour in.

Simple Remedies

DISEASE never comes without a cause. The way is prepared, and disease invited, by disregard of the laws of health. Many suffer in consequence of the transgression of their parents. While they are not responsible for what their parents have done, it is nevertheless their duty to ascertain what are and what are not violations of the laws of health. They should avoid the wrong habits of their parents, and, by correct living, place themselves in better conditions.

The greater number, however, suffer because of their own wrong course of action. They disregard the principles of health by their habits of eating, drinking, dressing, and working. Their transgression of nature's laws produces the sure result; and when sickness comes upon them, many do not credit their suffering to the true cause, but murmur against God because of their afflictions. But God is not responsible for the suffering that follows disregard of natural law.

God has endowed us with a certain amount of vital force. He has also formed us with organs suited to maintain the various functions of life, and He designs that these organs shall work together in harmony. If we carefully preserve the life force, and keep the delicate mechanism of the body in order, the result is health; but if the vital force is too rapidly exhausted, the nervous system borrows power for present use from its resources of strength, and when one organ is injured, all are affected. Nature bears much abuse without apparent resistance; she then arouses, and makes a determined effort to remove the effects of the ill-treatment she has suffered. Her effort to correct these conditions is often manifest in fever and various other forms of sickness.

When the abuse of health is carried so far that sickness results, the sufferer can often do for himself what no one else can do for him. The first thing to be done is to ascertain the true character of the sickness, and then go to work intelligently to remove the cause. If the harmonious working of the system has become unbalanced by overwork, overeating, or other irregularities, do not endeavor to adjust the difficulties by adding a burden of poisonous medicines.

Beware of Patent Medicines

A practice that is laying the foundation of a vast amount of disease and of even more serious evils, is the free use of poisonous drugs. When attacked by disease, many will not take the trouble to search out the cause of their illness. Their chief anxiety is to rid themselves of pain and inconvenience. So they resort to patent nostrums, of whose real properties they know little, or they apply to a physician for some remedy to counteract the result of their misdoing, but with no thought of making a change in their unhealthful habits. If immediate benefit is not realized, another medicine is tried, and then another. Thus the evil continues.

Disease is an effort of nature to free the system from conditions that result from a violation of the laws of health.

128

In case of sickness, the cause should be ascertained. Unhealthful conditions should be changed, wrong habits corrected. Then nature is to be assisted in her effort to expel impurities and to reestablish right conditions in the system.

Intemperate eating is often the cause of sickness, and what nature most needs is to be relieved of the undue burden that has been placed upon her. In many cases of sickness the very best remedy is for the patient to fast for a meal or two, that the overworked organs of digestion may have an opportunity to rest. A fruit diet for a few days has often brought great relief to brainworkers. Many times a short period of entire abstinence from food, followed by simple, moderate eating, has led to recovery through nature's own recuperative effort. An abstemious diet for a month or two would convince many sufferers that the path of self-denial is the path to health.

Some make themselves sick by overwork. For these, rest, freedom from care, and a spare diet are essential to restoration of health. To those who are brain weary and nervous because of continual labor and close confinement, a visit to the country, where they can live a simple, carefree life, coming in close contact with the things of nature, will be most helpful. Roaming through the fields and the woods, picking the flowers, listening to the songs of the birds, will do far more than any other agency toward their recovery.

Intelligent Use of Water

In health and in sickness, pure water is one of heaven's choicest blessings. Its proper use promotes health. It is the beverage which God provided to quench the thirst of

129

animals and man. Drunk freely, it helps to supply the necessities of the system, and assists nature to resist disease. The external application of water is one of the easiest and most satisfactory ways of regulating the circulation of the blood. A cold or cool bath is an excellent tonic. Warm baths open the pores, and thus aid in the elimination of impurities. Both warm and neutral baths soothe the nerves and equalize the circulation.

But many have never learned by experience the beneficial effects of the proper use of water, and they are afraid of it. Water treatments are not appreciated as they should be, and to apply them skillfully requires work that many are unwilling to perform. But none should feel excused for ignorance or indifference on this subject. There are many ways in which water can be applied to relieve pain, and check disease. All should become intelligent in its use in simple home treatments. Mothers, especially, should know how to care for their families in both health and sickness.

Value of Exercise

Action is a law of our being. Every organ of the body has its appointed work, upon the performance of which its development and strength depend. The normal action of all the organs gives strength and vigor, while the tendency of disuse is toward decay and death. Bind up an arm, even for a few weeks, then free it from its bands, and you will see that it is weaker than the one you have been using moderately during the same time. Inactivity produces the same effect upon the whole muscular system.

Inactivity is a fruitful cause of disease. Exercise quickens and equalizes the circulation of the blood, but in idleness the blood does not circulate freely, and the changes in it, so necessary to life and health, do not take place. The skin, too, becomes inactive. Impurities are not expelled as they would be if the circulation had been quickened by vigorous exercise, the skin kept in a healthy condition, and the lungs fed with plenty of pure, fresh air. This state of the system throws a double burden on the excretory organs, and disease is the result.

Invalids should not be encouraged in inactivity. When there has been serious overtaxation in any direction, entire rest for a time will sometimes ward off serious illness; but in the case of confirmed invalids it is seldom necessary to suspend all activity.

Those who have broken down from mental labor should have rest from wearing thought, but they should not be led to believe that it is dangerous to use their mental powers at all. Many are inclined to regard their condition as worse than it really is. This state of mind is unfavorable to recovery, and should not be encouraged.

Ministers, teachers, students, and other brainworkers often suffer from illness as the result of severe mental taxation, unrelieved by physical exercise. What these persons need is a more active life. Strictly temperate habits, combined with proper exercise, would ensure both mental and physical vigor, and would give power of endurance to all brainworkers.

Those who have overtaxed their physical powers should not be encouraged to forgo manual labor entirely. But labor, to be of the greatest advantage, should be systematic and agreeable. Outdoor exercise is the best; it should be so planned as to strengthen by use the organs that have

131

become weakened; and the heart should be in it; the labor of the hands should never degenerate into mere drudgery.

When invalids have nothing to occupy their time and attention, their thoughts become centered upon themselves, and they grow morbid and irritable. Many times they dwell upon their bad feelings until they think themselves much worse than they really are, and wholly unable to do anything.

In all these cases, well-directed physical exercise would prove an effective remedial agent. In some cases it is indispensable to the recovery of health. The will goes with the labor of the hands, and what these invalids need is to have the will aroused. When the will is dormant, the imagination becomes abnormal, and it is impossible to resist disease.

Results of Inactivity

Inactivity is the greatest curse that could come upon most invalids. Light employment in useful labor, while it does not tax mind or body, has a happy influence upon both. It strengthens the muscles, improves the circulation, and gives the invalid the satisfaction of knowing that he is not wholly useless in this busy world. He may be able to do but little at first, but he will soon find his strength increasing, and the amount of work done can be increased accordingly.

Exercise aids the dyspeptic by giving the digestive organs a healthy tone. To engage in severe study or violent physical exercise immediately after eating hinders the work of digestion; but a short walk after a meal, with the head erect and the shoulders back, is a great benefit.

Notwithstanding all that is said and written concerning

its importance, there are still many who neglect physical exercise. Some grow corpulent because the system is clogged; others become thin and feeble because their vital powers are exhausted in disposing of an excess of food. The liver is burdened in its effort to cleanse the blood of impurities, and illness is the result.

Those whose habits are sedentary should, when the weather will permit, exercise in the open air every day, summer or winter. Walking is preferable to riding or driving, for it brings more of the muscles into exercise. The lungs are forced into healthy action, since it is impossible to walk briskly without inflating them.

Such exercise would in many cases be better for the health than medicine. Physicians often advise their patients to take an ocean voyage, to go to some mineral spring, or to visit different places for change of climate, when in most cases if they would eat temperately, and take cheerful, healthful exercise, they would recover health, and would save time and money.

Home Nursing

THOSE who minister to the sick should understand the importance of careful attention to the laws of health. Nowhere is obedience to these laws more important than in the sickroom. Nowhere does so much depend upon faithfulness in little things on the part of the attendants. In cases of serious illness, a little neglect, a slight inattention to a patient's special needs or dangers, the manifestation of fear, excitement, or petulance, even a lack of sympathy, may turn the scale that is balancing life and death, and cause to go down to the grave a patient who otherwise might have recovered.

The efficiency of the nurse depends, to a great degree, upon physical vigor. The better the health the better will she be able to endure the strain of attendance upon the sick, and the more successfully can she perform her duties. Those who care for the sick should give special attention to diet, cleanliness, fresh air, and exercise. Like carefulness on the part of the family will enable them also to endure the extra burdens brought upon them, and will help to prevent them from contracting disease.

Where the illness is serious, requiring the attendance of a nurse night and day, the work should be shared by at least two efficient nurses, so that each may have opportunity for rest and for exercise in the open air. This is especially important in cases where it is difficult to secure an abundance of fresh air in the sickroom. Through ignorance of the importance of fresh air, ventilation is sometimes restricted, and the lives of both patient and attendant are often in danger.

If proper precaution is observed, noncontagious diseases need not be taken by others. Let the habits be correct, and by cleanliness and proper ventilation keep the sickroom free from poisonous elements. Under such conditions the sick are much more likely to recover, and in most cases neither attendants nor the members of the family will contract the disease.

To afford the patient the most favorable conditions for recovery, the room he occupies should be large, light, and cheerful, with opportunity for thorough ventilation. The room in the house that best meets these requirements should be chosen as the sickroom. Many houses have no special provision for proper ventilation, and to secure it is difficult; but every possible effort should be made to arrange the sickroom so that a current of fresh air can pass through it night and day.

Temperature in the Sickroom

So far as possible, an even temperature should be maintained in the sickroom. The thermometer should be consulted. Those who have the care of the sick, being often deprived of sleep or awakened in the night to attend to the patient, are liable to chilliness, and are not good judges of a healthful temperature.

An important part of the nurse's duty is the care of the

patient's diet. The patient should not be allowed to suffer or become unduly weakened through lack of nourishment, nor should the enfeebled digestive powers be overtaxed. Care should be taken so to prepare and serve the food that it will be palatable, but wise judgment should be used in adapting it to the needs of the patient, both in quantity and quality. In times of convalescence, especially, when the appetite is keen, before the digestive organs have recovered strength, there is great danger of injury from errors in diet.

Nurses, and all who have to do with the sickroom, should be cheerful, calm, and self-possessed. All hurry, excitement, or confusion should be avoided. Doors should be opened and shut with care, and the whole household be kept quiet. In cases of fever, special care is needed when the crisis comes and the fever is passing away. Then constant watching is often necessary. Ignorance, forgetfulness, and recklessness have caused the death of many who might have lived had they received proper care from judicious, thoughtful nurses.

It is misdirected kindness, a false idea of courtesy, that leads to much visiting of the sick. Those who are very ill should not have visitors. The excitement connected with receiving callers wearies the patient at a time when he is in the greatest need of quiet, undisturbed rest.

To a convalescent or a patient suffering from chronic disease, it is often a pleasure and a benefit to know that he is kindly remembered; but this assurance conveyed by a message of sympathy or by some little gift will often serve a better purpose than a personal visit, and without danger of harm.

136

The Mental Outlook

THE relation that exists between the mind and the body is very intimate. When one is affected, the other sympathizes. The condition of the mind affects the health to a far greater degree than many realize. Many of the diseases from which men suffer are the result of mental depression. Grief, anxiety, discontent, remorse, guilt, distrust—all tend to break down the life forces and to invite decay and death.

Disease is sometimes produced, and is often greatly aggravated, by the imagination. Many are lifelong invalids who might be well if they only thought so. Many imagine that every slight exposure will cause illness, and the evil effect is produced because it is expected. Many die from disease the cause of which is wholly imaginary.

Courage, hope, faith, sympathy, love, promote health and prolong life. A contented mind, a cheerful spirit, is health to the body and strength to the soul. "A merry [rejoicing] heart doeth good like a medicine." Proverbs 17:22.

In the treatment of the sick, the effect of mental influence should not be overlooked. Rightly used, this influence affords one of the most effective agencies for combating disease.

There is, however, a form of mind cure that is one of

137

the most effective agencies for evil. Through this so-called science one mind is brought under the control of another, so that the individuality of the weaker is merged in that of the stronger mind. One person acts out the will of another. Thus it is claimed that the tenor of the thoughts may be changed, that health-giving impulses may be imparted, and patients may be enabled to resist and overcome disease.

This method of cure has been employed by persons who were ignorant of its real nature and tendency, and who believed it to be a means of benefit to the sick. But the so-called science is based upon false principles. It is foreign to the nature and spirit of Christ. It does not lead to Him who is life and salvation. The one who attracts minds to himself leads them to separate from the true Source of their strength.

It is not God's purpose that any human being should yield his mind and will to the control of another, becoming a passive instrument in his hands. No one is to merge his individuality in that of another. He is not to look to any human being as the source of healing. His dependence must be in God. In the dignity of his God-given manhood he is to be controlled by God Himself, not by any human intelligence.

The Principle of Personal Responsibility

God desires to bring men into direct relation with Himself. In all His dealings with human beings He recognizes the principle of personal responsibility. He seeks to encourage a sense of personal dependence, and to impress the need of personal guidance. He desires to bring the human into association with the divine, that men may be transformed into the divine likeness. Satan works to thwart this purpose. He seeks to encourage dependence upon men. When minds are turned away from God, the tempter can bring them under his rule. He can control humanity.

The theory of mind controlling mind was originated by Satan, to introduce himself as the chief worker, to put human philosophy where divine philosophy should be. Of all the errors that are finding acceptance among professedly Christian people, none is a more dangerous deception, none more certain to separate man from God, than is this. Innocent though it may appear, if exercised upon patients it will tend to their destruction, not to their restoration. It opens a door through which Satan will enter to take possession both of the mind that is given up to be controlled by another, and of the mind that controls.

Fearful is the power thus given to evil-minded men and women. What opportunities it affords to those who live by taking advantage of others' weaknesses or follies! How many, through control of minds feeble or diseased, will find a means of gratifying lustful passion or greed of gain!

There is something better for us to engage in than the control of humanity by humanity. The physician should educate the people to look from the human to the divine. Instead of teaching the sick to depend upon human beings for the cure of soul and body, he should direct them to the One who can save to the uttermost all who come unto Him. He who made man's mind knows what the mind needs. God alone is the One who can heal. Those whose minds and bodies are diseased are to behold in Christ the restorer. "Because I live," He says, "ye shall live also."

139

John 14:19. This is the life we are to present to the sick, telling them that if they have faith in Christ as the restorer, if they cooperate with Him, obeying the laws of health and striving to perfect holiness in His fear, He will impart to them His life. When we present Christ to them in this way we are imparting a power, a strength, that is of value; for it comes from above. This is the true science of healing for body and soul.

Faith in the Great Physician

Great wisdom is needed in dealing with diseases caused through the mind. A sore, sick heart, a discouraged mind, needs mild treatment. Many times some living home trouble is, like a canker, eating to the very soul and weakening the life force. And sometimes it is the case that remorse for sin undermines the constitution and unbalances the mind. It is through tender sympathy that this class of invalids can be benefited. The physician should first gain their confidence, and then point them to the Great Healer. If their faith can be directed to the True Physician, and they can have confidence that He has undertaken their case, this will bring relief to the mind, and often give health to the body.

Sympathy and tact will often prove a greater benefit to the sick than will the most skillful treatment given in a cold, indifferent way.

Many, fearing to excite or discourage a patient by stating the truth, will hold out false hopes of recovery, and even allow a patient to go down to the grave without warning him of his danger. All this is unwise. It may not always be safe or best to explain to the patient the full extent

140

of his danger. This might alarm him and retard or even prevent recovery. Nor can the whole truth always be told to those whose ailments are largely imaginary. Many of these persons are unreasonable, and have not accustomed themselves to exercise self-control. They have peculiar fancies, and imagine many things that are false in regard to themselves and to others. To them these things are real, and those who care for them need to manifest constant kindness and unwearied patience and tact. If these patients were told the truth in regard to themselves, some would be offended, others discouraged. Christ said to His disciples, "I have yet many things to say unto you, but ye cannot bear them now." John 16:12. But though the truth may not all be spoken on all occasions, it is never necessary or justifiable to deceive.

Power of the Will

The power of the will is not valued as it should be. Let the will be kept awake and rightly directed, and it will impart energy to the whole being, and will be a wonderful aid in the maintenance of health. It is a power also in dealing with disease. Exercised in the right direction, it would control the imagination, and be a potent means of resisting and overcoming disease of both mind and body. By the exercise of the willpower in placing themselves in right relation to life, patients can do much to cooperate with the physician's efforts for their recovery. There are thousands who can recover health if they will. The Lord does not want them to be sick. He desires them to be well and happy, and they should make up their minds to be well. Often invalids can resist disease simply by refusing to yield to ailments and settle down in a state of inactivity. Rising above their aches and pains, let them engage in useful employment suited to their strength. By such employment and the free use of air and sunlight, many an emaciated invalid might recover health and strength.

For those who would regain or preserve health there is a lesson in the words of Scripture, "Be not drunk with wine, wherein is excess; but be filled with the Spirit." Ephesians 5:18. Not through the excitement or oblivion produced by unnatural or unhealthful stimulants; not through indulgence of the lower appetites or passions, is to be found true healing or refreshment for the body or the soul. Among the sick are many who are without God and without hope. They suffer from ungratified desires, disordered passions, and the condemnation of their own consciences; they are losing their hold upon this life, and they have no prospect for the life to come. Let not the attendants upon the sick hope to benefit these patients by granting them frivolous, exciting indulgences. These have been the curse of their lives. The hungry, thirsting soul will continue to hunger and thirst so long as it seeks to find satisfaction here. Those who drink at the fountain of selfish pleasure are deceived. They mistake hilarity for strength, and when the excitement ceases their inspiration ends, and they are left to discontent and despondency.

The Source of All Peace

Abiding peace, true rest of spirit, has but one Source. It was of this that Christ spoke when He said, "Come unto Me, all ye that labor and are heavy-laden, and I will give you rest." Matthew 11:28. "Peace I leave with you, My peace I give unto you: not as the world giveth, give I unto you." John 14:27. This peace is not something that He gives apart from Himself. It is in Christ, and we can receive it only by receiving Him.

Christ is the wellspring of life. That which many need is to have a clearer knowledge of Him; they need to be patiently and kindly, yet earnestly, taught how the whole being may be thrown open to the healing agencies of heaven. When the sunlight of God's love illuminates the darkened chambers of the soul, restless weariness and dissatisfaction will cease, and satisfying joys will give vigor to the mind and health and energy to the body.

We are in a world of suffering. Difficulty, trial, and sorrow await us all along the way to the heavenly home. But there are many who make life's burdens doubly heavy by continually anticipating trouble. If they meet with adversity or disappointment, they think that everything is going to ruin, that theirs is the hardest lot of all, that they are surely coming to want. Thus they bring wretchedness upon themselves and cast a shadow upon all around them. Life itself becomes a burden to them. But it need not be thus. It will cost a determined effort to change the current of their thought. But the change can be made. Their happiness, both for this life and for the life to come, depends upon their fixing their minds upon cheerful things. Let them look away from the dark picture, which is imaginary, to the benefits which God has strewn in their pathway, and beyond these to the unseen and eternal.

For every trial, God has provided help. When Israel in the desert came to the bitter waters of Marah, Moses cried unto the Lord. The Lord did not provide some new remedy; He called attention to that which was at hand. A shrub which He had created was to be cast into the fountain to make the water pure and sweet. When this was done, the people drank of the water and were refreshed. In every trial, if we seek Him, Christ will give us help. Our eyes will be opened to discern the healing promises recorded in His Word. The Holy Spirit will teach us how to appropriate every blessing that will be an antidote to grief. For every bitter draft that is placed to our lips we shall find a branch of healing.

Take Hold of God's Strength

We are not to let the future, with its hard problems, its unsatisfying prospects, make our hearts faint, our knees tremble, our hands hang down. "Let him take hold of My strength," says the Mighty One, "that he may make peace with Me; and he shall make peace with Me." Isaiah 27:5. Those who surrender their lives to His guidance and to His service will never be placed in a position for which He has not made provision. Whatever our situation, if we are doers of His Word, we have a Guide to direct our way; whatever our perplexity, we have a sure Counselor; whatever our sorrow, bereavement, or loneliness, we have a sympathizing Friend.

If in our ignorance we make missteps, the Saviour does not forsake us. We need never feel that we are alone. Angels are our companions. The Comforter that Christ promised to send in His name abides with us. In the way that leads to the City of God there are no difficulties which those who trust in Him may not overcome. There are no dangers which they may not escape. There is not a sorrow,

144

not a grievance, not a human weakness, for which He has not provided a remedy.

He Waits to Make Us Free

None need abandon themselves to discouragement and despair. Satan may come to you with the cruel suggestion, Yours is a hopeless case; you are irredeemable. But there is hope for you in Christ. God does not bid us overcome in our own strength. He asks us to come close to His side. Whatever difficulties we labor under, which weigh down soul and body, He waits to make us free.

He who took humanity upon Himself knows how to sympathize with the sufferings of humanity. Not only does Christ know every soul, and the peculiar needs and trials of that soul, but He knows all the circumstances that chafe and perplex the spirit. His hand is outstretched in pitying tenderness to every suffering child. Those who suffer most have most of His sympathy and pity. He is touched with the feeling of our infirmities, and He desires us to lay our perplexities and troubles at His feet, and leave them there.

It is not wise to look to ourselves and study our emotions. If we do this, the enemy will present difficulties and temptations that weaken faith and destroy courage. Closely to study our emotions and give way to our feelings is to entertain doubt and entangle ourselves in perplexity. We are to look away from self to Jesus.

When temptations assail you, when care, perplexity, and darkness seem to surround your soul, look to the place where you last saw the light. Rest in Christ's love and under His protecting care. When sin struggles for the mastery in the heart, when guilt oppresses the soul and burdens the conscience, when unbelief clouds the mind, remember that Christ's grace is sufficient to subdue sin and banish the darkness. Entering into communion with the Saviour, we enter the region of peace.

The Spirit of Gratitude

Nothing tends more to promote health of body and of soul than does a spirit of gratitude and praise. It is a positive duty to resist melancholy, discontented thoughts and feelings—as much a duty as it is to pray. If we are heaven-bound, how can we go as a band of mourners, groaning and complaining all along the way to our Father's house?

Those professed Christians who are constantly complaining, and who seem to think cheerfulness and happiness a sin, have not genuine religion. Those who take a mournful pleasure in all that is melancholy in the natural world, who choose to look upon dead leaves rather than to gather the beautiful living flowers, who see no beauty in grand mountain heights and in valleys clothed with living green, who close their senses to the joyful voice which speaks to them in nature, and which is sweet and musical to the listening ear—these are not in Christ. They are gathering to themselves gloom and darkness, when they might have brightness, even the Sun of Righteousness arising in their hearts with healing in His beams.

Often your mind may be clouded because of pain. Then do not try to think. You know that Jesus loves you. He understands your weakness. You may do His will by simply resting in His arms.

It is a law of nature that our thoughts and feelings are encouraged and strengthened as we give them utterance.

While words express thoughts, it is also true that thoughts follow words. If we would give more expression to our faith, rejoice more in the blessings that we know we have —the great mercy and love of God—we should have more faith and greater joy. No tongue can express, no finite mind can conceive, the blessing that results from appreciating the goodness and love of God. Even on earth we may have joy as a wellspring—never failing, because fed by the streams that flow from the throne of God.

Then let us educate our hearts and lips to speak the praise of God for His matchless love. Let us educate our souls to be hopeful and to abide in the light shining from the cross of Calvary. Never should we forget that we are children of the heavenly King, sons and daughters of the Lord of hosts. It is our privilege to maintain a calm repose in God.

"Let the peace of God rule in your hearts; . . . and be ye thankful." Colossians 3:15. Forgetting our own difficulties and troubles, let us praise God for an opportunity to live for the glory of His name. Let the fresh blessings of each new day awaken praise in our hearts for these tokens of His loving care. When you open your eyes in the morning, thank God that He has kept you through the night. Thank Him for His peace in your heart. Morning, noon, and night, let gratitude as a sweet perfume ascend to heaven.

When someone asks how you are feeling, do not try to think of something mournful to tell in order to gain sympathy. Do not talk of your lack of faith and your sorrows and sufferings. The tempter delights to hear such words. When talking on gloomy subjects, you are glorifying him. We are not to dwell on the great power of Satan to overcome us. Often we give ourselves into his hands by talking of his power. Let us talk instead of the great power of God to bind up all our interests with His own. Tell of the matchless power of Christ and speak of His glory. All heaven is interested in our salvation. The angels of God, thousands upon thousands, and ten thousand times ten thousand, are commissioned to minister to those who shall be heirs of salvation. They guard us against evil, and press back the powers of darkness that are seeking our destruction. Have we not reason to be thankful every moment, thankful even when there are apparent difficulties in our pathway?

Lift Up a Song

Let praise and thanksgiving be expressed in song. When tempted, instead of giving utterance to our feelings, let us by faith lift up a song of thanksgiving to God.

Song is a weapon that we can always use against discouragement. As we thus open the heart to the sunlight of the Saviour's presence, we shall have health and His blessing.

> "Give thanks unto the Lord, for He is good:
> For His mercy endureth forever.
> Let the redeemed of the Lord say so,
> Whom He hath redeemed from the hand of the enemy."
> Psalm 107:1, 2.

"In everything give thanks: for this is the will of God in Christ Jesus concerning you." 1 Thessalonians 5:18. This command is an assurance that even the things which appear to be against us will work for our good. God would not bid us be thankful for that which would do us harm.

One of the surest hindrances to the recovery of the sick is the centering of attention upon themselves. Many invalids

148

feel that everyone should give them sympathy and help, when what they need is to have their attention turned away from themselves, to think of and care for others.

Often prayer is solicited for the afflicted, the sorrowful, the discouraged; and this is right. We should pray that God will shed light into the darkened mind, and comfort the sorrowful heart. But God answers prayer for those who place themselves in the channel of His blessings. While we offer prayer for these sorrowful ones, we should encourage them to try to help those more needy than themselves. The darkness will be dispelled from their own hearts as they try to help others. As we seek to comfort others with the comfort wherewith we are comforted, the blessing comes back to us.

The fifty-eighth chapter of Isaiah is a prescription for maladies of the body and of the soul. If we desire health and the true joy of life, we must put into practice the rules given in this scripture. Of the service acceptable to Him, and its blessings, the Lord says:

"Is it not to deal thy bread to the hungry,
And that thou bring the poor that are cast out to thy
    house?
When thou seest the naked, that thou cover him;
And that thou hide not thyself from thine own flesh?
Then shall thy light break forth as the morning,
And thine health shall spring forth speedily:
And thy righteousness shall go before thee;
The glory of the Lord shall be thy rearward."
                    Isaiah 58:7, 8.

Good deeds are twice a blessing, benefiting both the giver and the receiver of the kindness. The consciousness of right-doing is one of the best medicines for diseased bodies and minds. When the mind is free and happy from a sense of duty well done and the satisfaction of giving happiness to others, the cheering, uplifting influence brings new life to the whole being.

If those who are suffering from ill health would forget self in their interest for others, if they would fulfill the Lord's command to minister to those more needy than themselves, they would realize the truthfulness of the prophetic promise, "Then shall thy light break forth as the morning, and thine health shall spring forth speedily."

Benefits of Outdoor Life

THE Creator chose for our first parents the surroundings best adapted for their health and happiness. He did not place them in a palace, or surround them with the artificial adornments and luxuries that so many today are struggling to obtain. He placed them in close touch with nature, and in close communion with the holy ones of heaven.

In the garden that God prepared as a home for His children, graceful shrubs and delicate flowers greeted the eye at every turn. There were trees of every variety, many of them laden with fragrant and delicious fruit. On their branches the birds caroled their songs of praise. Under their shadow the creatures of the earth sported together without a fear.

Adam and Eve, in their untainted purity, delighted in the sights and sounds of Eden. God appointed them their work in the garden, "to dress it and to keep it." Genesis 2:15. Each day's labor brought them health and gladness, and the happy pair greeted with joy the visits of their Creator, as in the cool of the day He walked and talked with them. Daily God taught them His lessons.

The plan of life which God appointed for our first parents has lessons for us. Although sin has cast its shadow over the earth, God desires His children to find delight in the works of His hands. The more closely His plan of life is followed the more wonderfully will He work to restore suffering humanity. The sick need to be brought into close touch with nature. An outdoor life amid natural surroundings would work wonders for many a helpless and almost hopeless invalid.

The noise and excitement and confusion of the cities, their constrained and artificial life, are most wearisome and exhausting to the sick. The air, laden with smoke and dust, with poisonous gases, and with germs of disease, is a peril to life. The sick, for the most part shut within four walls, come almost to feel as if they were prisoners in their rooms. They look out on houses and pavements and hurrying crowds, with perhaps not even a glimpse of blue sky or sunshine, or grass or flower or tree. Shut up in this way, they brood over their suffering and sorrow, and become a prey to their own sad thoughts.

Danger in the Cities

And for those who are weak in moral power, the cities abound in dangers. In them, patients who have unnatural appetites to overcome are continually exposed to temptation. They need to be placed amid new surroundings where the current of their thoughts will be changed; they need to be placed under influences wholly different from those that have wrecked their lives. Let them for a season be removed from those influences that lead away from God, into a purer atmosphere.

Institutions for the care of the sick would be far more successful if they could be established away from the cities.

And so far as possible, all who are seeking to recover health should place themselves amid country surroundings, where they can have the benefit of outdoor life. Nature is God's physician. The pure air, the glad sunshine, the flowers and trees, the orchards and vineyards, and outdoor exercise amid these surroundings, are health-giving, life-giving.

Physicians and nurses should encourage their patients to be much in the open air. Outdoor life is the only remedy that many invalids need. It has a wonderful power to heal diseases caused by the excitements and excesses of fashionable life, a life that weakens and destroys the powers of body, mind, and soul.

How grateful to the invalids weary of city life, the glare of many lights, and the noise of the streets, are the quiet and freedom of the country! How eagerly do they turn to the scenes of nature! How glad would they be to sit in the open air, rejoice in the sunshine, and breathe the fragrance of tree and flower! There are life-giving properties in the balsam of the pine, in the fragrance of the cedar and the fir, and other trees also have properties that are health restoring.

To the chronic invalid nothing so tends to restore health and happiness as living amid attractive country surroundings. Here the most helpless ones can sit or lie in the sunshine or in the shade of the trees. They have only to lift their eyes to see above them the beautiful foliage. A sweet sense of restfulness and refreshing comes over them as they listen to the murmuring of the breezes. The drooping spirits revive. The waning strength is recruited. Unconsciously the mind becomes peaceful, the fevered pulse more calm and regular. As the sick grow stronger, they will venture to take a few steps to gather some of the lovely flowers, precious messengers of God's love to His afflicted family here below.

Plans should be devised for keeping patients out of doors. For those who are able to work, let some pleasant, easy employment be provided. Show them how agreeable and helpful this outdoor work is. Encourage them to breathe the fresh air. Teach them to breathe deeply, and in breathing and speaking to exercise the abdominal muscles. This is an education that will be invaluable to them.

Exercise in the open air should be prescribed as a life-giving necessity. And for such exercises there is nothing better than the cultivation of the soil. Let patients have flower beds to care for, or work to do in the orchard or vegetable garden. As they are encouraged to leave their rooms and spend time in the open air, cultivating flowers or doing some other light, pleasant work, their attention will be diverted from themselves and their sufferings.

The more the patient can be kept out of doors, the less care will he require. The more cheerful his surroundings, the more hopeful will he be. Shut up in the house, be it ever so elegantly furnished, he will grow fretful and gloomy. Surround him with the beautiful things of nature; place him where he can see the flowers growing and hear the birds singing, and his heart will break into song in harmony with the songs of the birds. Relief will come to body and mind. The intellect will be awakened, the imagination quickened, and the mind prepared to appreciate the beauty of God's Word.

Reminders of the Better World

In nature may always be found something to divert the attention of the sick from themselves and direct their thoughts to God. Surrounded by His wonderful works, their minds are uplifted from the things that are seen to the things that are unseen. The beauty of nature leads them to think of the heavenly home, where there will be nothing to mar the loveliness, nothing to taint or destroy, nothing to cause disease or death.

Under such influences as these, many suffering ones will be guided into the way of life. Angels of heaven cooperate with human instrumentalities in bringing encouragement and hope and joy and peace to the hearts of the sick and suffering. Under such conditions the sick are doubly blessed, and many find health. The feeble step recovers its elasticity. The eye regains its brightness. The hopeless become hopeful. The once despondent countenance wears an expression of joy. The complaining tones of the voice give place to tones of cheerfulness and content.

As physical health is regained men and women are better able to exercise that faith in Christ which secures the health of the soul. In the consciousness of sins forgiven there is inexpressible peace and joy and rest. The clouded hope of the Christian is brightened. The words express the belief, "God is our refuge and strength, a very present help in trouble." Psalm 46:1. "Yea, though I walk through the valley of the shadow of death, I will fear no evil: for Thou art with me; Thy rod and Thy staff they comfort me." Psalm 23:4. "He giveth power to the faint; and to them that have no might He increaseth strength." Isaiah 40:29.

The Power of Prayer

THE Scripture says that "Men ought always to pray, and not to faint" (Luke 18:1); and if ever there is a time when they feel their need of prayer, it is when strength fails, and life itself seems slipping from their grasp. Often those who are in health forget the wonderful mercies continued to them day by day, year after year, and they render no tribute of praise to God for His benefits. But when sickness comes, God is remembered. When human strength fails, men feel their need of divine help. And never does our merciful God turn from the soul that in sincerity seeks Him for help. He is our refuge in sickness as in health.

Christ is the same compassionate physician now that He was during His earthly ministry. In Him there is healing balm for every disease, restoring power for every infirmity. His disciples in this time are to pray for the sick as verily as the disciples of old prayed. And recoveries will follow; for "the prayer of faith shall save the sick." We have the Holy Spirit's power, the calm assurance of faith, that can claim God's promises. The Lord's promise, "They shall lay hands on the sick, and they shall recover" (Mark 16:18), is just as trustworthy now as in the days of the apostles. It presents the privilege of God's children, and our faith should lay hold of all that it embraces. Christ's ser-

156

vants are the channel of His working, and through them He desires to exercise His healing power. It is our work to present the sick and suffering to God in the arms of our faith. We should teach them to believe in the Great Healer.

The Saviour would have us encourage the sick, the hopeless, the afflicted, to take hold upon His strength. Through faith and prayer the sickroom may be transformed into a Bethel. In word and deed, physicians and nurses may say, so plainly that it cannot be misunderstood, "The Lord is in this place" to save, and not to destroy. Christ desires to manifest His presence in the sickroom, filling the hearts of physicians and nurses with the sweetness of His love. If the life of the attendants upon the sick is such that Christ can go with them to the bedside of the patient, there will come to him the conviction that the compassionate Saviour is present, and this conviction will itself do much for the healing of both the soul and the body.

God Hears Prayer

And God hears prayer. Christ has said, "If ye shall ask anything in My name, I will do it." John 14:14. Again He says, "If any man serve Me, him will My Father honor." John 12:26. If we live according to His Word, every precious promise He has given will be fulfilled to us. We are undeserving of His mercy, but as we give ourselves to Him, He receives us. He will work for and through those who follow Him.

But only as we live in obedience to His Word can we claim the fulfillment of His promises. The psalmist says, "If I regard iniquity in my heart, the Lord will not hear me." Psalm 66:18. If we render to Him only a partial half-hearted obedience, His promises will not be fulfilled to us.

In the Word of God we have instruction relative to special prayer for the recovery of the sick. But the offering of such prayer is a most solemn act, and should not be entered upon without careful consideration. In many cases of prayer for the healing of the sick, that which is called faith is nothing less than presumption.

Many persons bring disease upon themselves by their self-indulgence. They have not lived in accordance with natural law or the principles of strict purity. Others have disregarded the laws of health in their habits of eating and drinking, dressing, or working. Often some form of vice is the cause of feebleness of mind or body. Should these persons gain the blessing of health, many of them would continue to pursue the same course of heedless transgression of God's natural and spiritual laws, reasoning that if God heals them in answer to prayer, they are at liberty to continue their unhealthful practices and to indulge perverted appetite without restraint. If God were to work a miracle in restoring these persons to health, He would be encouraging sin.

It is labor lost to teach people to look to God as a healer of their infirmities, unless they are taught also to lay aside unhealthful practices. In order to receive His blessing in answer to prayer, they must cease to do evil and learn to do well. Their surroundings must be sanitary, their habits of life correct. They must live in harmony with the law of God, both natural and spiritual.

To those who desire prayer for their restoration to health, it should be made plain that the violation of God's law, either natural or spiritual, is sin, and that in order for them

158

to receive His blessing, sin must be confessed and forsaken.

The Scripture bids us, "Confess your faults one to another, and pray one for another, that ye may be healed." James 5:16. To the one asking for prayer, let thoughts like these be presented: "We cannot read the heart, or know the secrets of your life. These are known only to yourself and to God. If you repent of your sins, it is your duty to make confession of them." Sin of a private character is to be confessed to Christ, the only Mediator between God and man. For "if any man sin, we have an advocate with the Father, Jesus Christ the righteous." 1 John 2:1. Every sin is an offense against God, and is to be confessed to Him through Christ. Every open sin should be as openly confessed. Wrong done to a fellow being should be made right with the one who has been offended. If any who are seeking health have been guilty of evil speaking, if they have sowed discord in the home, the neighborhood, or the church, and have stirred up alienation and dissension, if by any wrong practice they have led others into sin, these things should be confessed before God and before those who have been offended. "If we confess our sins, He is faithful and just to forgive us our sins, and to cleanse us from all unrighteousness." 1 John 1:9.

When wrongs have been righted, we may present the needs of the sick to the Lord in calm faith, as His Spirit may indicate. He knows each individual by name, and cares for each as if there were not another upon the earth for whom He gave His beloved Son. Because God's love is so great and so unfailing, the sick should be encouraged to trust in Him and be cheerful. To be anxious about themselves tends to cause weakness and disease. If they will

159

rise above depression and gloom, their prospect of recovery will be better; for "the eye of the Lord is upon them . . . that hope in His mercy." Psalm 33:18.

Thy Will Be Done

In prayer for the sick, it should be remembered that "we know not what we should pray for as we ought." Romans 8:26. We do not know whether the blessing we desire will be best or not. Therefore our prayers should include this thought: "Lord, Thou knowest every secret of the soul. Thou art acquainted with these persons. Jesus, their Advocate, gave His life for them. His love for them is greater than ours can possibly be. If, therefore, it is for Thy glory and the good of the afflicted ones, we ask, in the name of Jesus, that they may be restored to health. If it be not Thy will that they may be restored, we ask that Thy grace may comfort and Thy presence sustain them in their sufferings."

God knows the end from the beginning. He is acquainted with the hearts of all men. He reads every secret of the soul. He knows whether those for whom prayer is offered would or would not be able to endure the trials that would come upon them should they live. He knows whether their lives would be a blessing or a curse to themselves and to the world. This is one reason why, while presenting our petitions with earnestness, we should say, "Nevertheless not my will, but Thine, be done." Luke 22:42. Jesus added these words of submission to the wisdom and will of God when in the Garden of Gethsemane He pleaded, "O My Father, if it be possible, let this cup pass from Me." Matthew 26:39. And if they were appropriate for Him, the

Son of God, how much more are they becoming on the lips of finite, erring mortals!

The consistent course is to commit our desires to our all-wise heavenly Father, and then, in perfect confidence, trust all to Him. We know that God hears us if we ask according to His will. But to press our petitions without a submissive spirit is not right; our prayers must take the form, not of command, but of intercession.

There are cases where God works decidedly by His divine power in the restoration of health. But not all the sick are healed. Many are laid away to sleep in Jesus. John on the Isle of Patmos was bidden to write: "Blessed are the dead which die in the Lord from henceforth: Yea, saith the Spirit, that they may rest from their labors; and their works do follow them." Revelation 14:13. From this we see that if persons are not raised to health, they should not on this account be judged as wanting in faith.

We all desire immediate and direct answers to our prayers, and are tempted to become discouraged when the answer is delayed or comes in an unlooked-for form. But God is too wise and good to answer our prayers always at just the time and in just the manner we desire. He will do more and better for us than to accomplish all our wishes. And because we can trust His wisdom and love, we should not ask Him to concede to our will, but should seek to enter into and accomplish His purpose. Our desires and interests should be lost in His will. These experiences that test faith are for our benefit. By them it is made manifest whether our faith is true and sincere, resting on the Word of God alone, or whether, depending on circumstances, it is uncertain and changeable. Faith is strengthened by exercise.

161

We must let patience have its perfect work, remembering that there are precious promises in the Scriptures for those who wait upon the Lord.

Not all understand these principles. Many who seek the Lord's healing mercy think that they must have a direct and immediate answer to their prayers or their faith is defective. For this reason, those who are weakened by disease need to be counseled wisely that they may act with discretion. They should not disregard their duty to the friends who may survive them, or neglect to employ nature's agencies for the restoration of health.

Often there is danger of error here. Believing that they will be healed in answer to prayer, some fear to do anything that might seem to indicate a lack of faith. But they should not neglect to set their affairs in order as they would desire to do if they expected to be removed by death. Nor should they fear to utter words of encouragement or counsel which at the parting hour they wish to speak to their loved ones.

Cooperate With God

Those who seek healing by prayer should not neglect to make use of the remedial agencies within their reach. It is not denial of faith to use such remedies as God has provided to alleviate pain and to aid nature in her work of restoration. It is no denial of faith to cooperate with God, and to place themselves in the condition most favorable to recovery. God has put it in our power to obtain a knowledge of the laws of life. This knowledge has been placed within our reach for use. We should employ every facility for the restoration of health, taking every advantage possible, working in harmony with natural laws. When we have prayed for the recovery of the sick, we can work with all the more energy, thanking God that we have the privilege of cooperating with Him, and asking His blessing on the means which He Himself has provided.

We have the sanction of the Word of God for the use of remedial agencies. Hezekiah, king of Judah, was sick, and a prophet of God brought him the message that he should die. He cried unto the Lord, and the Lord heard His servant, and sent him a message that fifteen years should be added to his life. Now, one word from God would have healed Hezekiah instantly; but special directions were given, "Let them take a lump of figs, and lay it for a plaster upon the boil, and he shall recover." Isaiah 38:21.

When we have prayed for the recovery of the sick, whatever the outcome of the case, let us not lose faith in God. If we are called upon to meet bereavement, let us accept the bitter cup, remembering that a Father's hand holds it to our lips. But should health be restored, it should not be forgotten that the recipient of healing mercy is placed under renewed obligation to the Creator. When the ten lepers were cleansed, only one returned to find Jesus and give Him glory. Let none of us be like the unthinking nine, whose hearts were untouched by the mercy of God. "Every good gift and every perfect gift is from above, and cometh down from the Father of lights, with whom is no variableness, neither shadow of turning." James 1:17.

A Servant of Humanity

OUR Lord Jesus Christ came to this world as the unwearied servant of man's necessity. He "took our infirmities, and bare our sicknesses" (Matthew 8:17), that He might minister to every need of humanity. The burden of disease and wretchedness and sin He came to remove. It was His mission to bring to men complete restoration; He came to give them health and peace and perfection of character.

Varied were the circumstances and needs of those who besought His aid, and none who came to Him went away unhelped. From Him flowed a stream of healing power, and in body and mind and soul men were made whole.

The Saviour's work was not restricted to any time or place. His compassion knew no limit. On so large a scale did He conduct His work of healing and teaching that there was no building in Palestine large enough to receive the multitude that thronged to Him. On the green hill slopes of Galilee, in the thoroughfares of travel, by the seashore, in the synagogues, and in every other place where the sick could be brought to Him, was to be found His hospital. In every city, every town, every village through which He

164

passed, He laid His hands upon the afflicted ones and healed them. Wherever there were hearts ready to receive His message, He comforted them with the assurance of their heavenly Father's love. All day He ministered to those who came to Him; in the evening He gave attention to such as through the day must toil to earn a pittance for the support of their families.

Jesus carried the awful weight of responsibility for the salvation of men. He knew that unless there was a decided change in the principles and purposes of the human race, all would be lost. This was the burden of His soul, and none could appreciate the weight that rested upon Him. Through childhood, youth, and manhood He walked alone. Yet it was heaven to be in His presence. Day by day He met trials and temptations; day by day He was brought into contact with evil, and witnessed its power upon those whom He was seeking to bless and to save. Yet He did not fail or become discouraged.

In all things He brought His wishes into strict abeyance to His mission. He glorified His life by making everything in it subordinate to the will of His Father. When in His youth His mother, finding Him in the school of the rabbis, said, "Son, why hast Thou thus dealt with us?" He answered—and His answer is the keynote of His lifework— "How is it that ye sought Me? wist ye not that I must be about My Father's business?" Luke 2:48, 49.

A Life of Self-Sacrifice

His life was one of constant self-sacrifice. He had no home in this world, except as the kindness of friends provided for Him as a wayfarer. He came to live in our behalf

165

the life of the poorest, and to walk and work among the needy and the suffering. Unrecognized and unhonored, He walked in and out among the people for whom He had done so much.

He was always patient and cheerful, and the afflicted hailed Him as a messenger of life and peace. He saw the needs of men and women, children and youth, and to all He gave the invitation, "Come unto Me."

During His ministry, Jesus devoted more time to healing the sick than to preaching. His miracles testified to the truth of His words, that He came not to destroy, but to save. Wherever He went, the tidings of His mercy preceded Him. Where He had passed, the objects of His compassion were rejoicing in health and making trial of their new-found powers. Crowds were collecting around them to hear from their lips the works that the Lord had wrought. His voice was the first sound that many had ever heard, His name the first word they had ever spoken, His face the first they had ever looked upon. Why should they not love Jesus, and sound His praise? As He passed through the towns and cities, He was like a vital current, diffusing life and joy.

> "The land of Zebulun and the land of Naphtali,
>   Toward the sea, beyond the Jordan,
>   Galilee of the nations,
>   The people that sat in darkness
>   Saw a great light,
>   And to them that sat in the region and shadow of death,
>   To them did light spring up."
>   Matthew 4:15, 16, A.R.V., margin.

The Saviour made each work of healing an occasion for implanting divine principles in the mind and soul. This was the purpose of His work. He imparted earthly blessings that He might incline the hearts of men to receive the gospel of His grace.

The Gospel to the Poor

Christ might have occupied the highest place among the teachers of the Jewish nation, but He preferred rather to take the gospel to the poor. He went from place to place that those in the highways and byways might hear the words of truth. By the sea, on the mountainside, in the streets of the city, in the synagogue, His voice was heard explaining the Scriptures. Often He taught in the outer court of the temple, that the Gentiles might hear His words.

So unlike the explanations of Scripture given by the scribes and Pharisees was Christ's teaching, that the attention of the people was arrested. The rabbis dwelt upon tradition, upon human theory and speculation. Often that which men had taught and written about the Scripture was put in place of the Scripture itself. The subject of Christ's teaching was the Word of God. He met questioners with a plain, "It is written," "Hath not the Scripture said?" "How readest thou?" At every opportunity when an interest was awakened by either friend or foe, He presented the Word. With clearness and power He proclaimed the gospel message. His words shed a flood of light on the teachings of patriarchs and prophets, and the Scriptures came to men as a new revelation. Never before had His hearers perceived in the Word of God such depth of meaning.

Never was there such an evangelist as Christ. He was the Majesty of heaven, but He humbled Himself to take our nature, that He might meet men where they were. To all people, rich and poor, free and bond, Christ, the Messenger of the covenant, brought the tidings of salvation. His fame as the Great Healer spread throughout Palestine. The sick came to the places through which He would pass, that they might call on Him for help. Hither, too, came many anxious to hear His words and to receive a touch of His hand. Thus He went from city to city, from town to town, preaching the gospel and healing the sick—the King of glory in the lowly garb of humanity.

He attended the great yearly festivals of the nation, and to the multitude absorbed in outward ceremony He spoke of heavenly things, bringing eternity within their view. To all He brought treasures from the storehouse of wisdom. He spoke to them in language so simple that they could not fail of understanding. By methods peculiarly His own, He helped all who were in sorrow and affliction. With tender, courteous grace, He ministered to the sin-sick soul, bringing healing and strength.

The prince of teachers, He sought access to the people by the pathway of their most familiar associations. He presented the truth in such a way that ever after it was to His hearers intertwined with their most hallowed recollections and sympathies. He taught in a way that made them feel the completeness of His identification with their interests and happiness. His instruction was so direct, His illustrations were so appropriate, His words so sympathetic and cheerful, that His hearers were charmed. The simplicity and earnestness with which He addressed the needy, hallowed every word.

What a busy life He led! Day by day He might have been seen entering the humble abodes of want and sorrow, speaking hope to the downcast and peace to the distressed. Gracious, tenderhearted, pitiful, He went about lifting up the bowed-down and comforting the sorrowful. Wherever He went, He carried blessing.

While He ministered to the poor, Jesus studied also to find ways of reaching the rich. He sought the acquaintance of the wealthy and cultured Pharisee, the Jewish nobleman, and the Roman ruler. He accepted their invitations, attended their feasts, made Himself familiar with their interests and occupations that He might gain access to their hearts and reveal to them the imperishable riches.

Ways of Reaching the Rich

Christ came to this world to show that by receiving power from on high, man can live an unsullied life. With unwearying patience and sympathetic helpfulness, He met men in their necessities. By the gentle touch of grace, He banished from the soul unrest and doubt, changing enmity to love, and unbelief to confidence.

He could say to whom He pleased, "Follow Me," and the one addressed arose and followed Him. The spell of the world's enchantment was broken. At the sound of His voice the spirit of greed and ambition fled from the heart, and men arose, emancipated, to follow the Saviour.

No Distinction of Race or Creed

Christ recognized no distinction of nationality or rank or creed. The scribes and Pharisees desired to make a local and a national benefit of the gifts of heaven, and to exclude the rest of God's family in the world. But Christ came to break down every wall of partition. He came to show that

169

His gift of mercy and love is as unconfined as the air, the light, or the showers of rain that refresh the earth.

The life of Christ established a religion in which there is no caste, a religion by which Jew and Gentile, free and bond, are linked in a common brotherhood, equal before God. No question of policy influenced His movements. He made no difference between neighbors and strangers, friends and enemies. That which appealed to His heart was a soul thirsting for the waters of life.

He passed by no human being as worthless, but sought to apply the healing remedy to every soul. In whatever company He found Himself, He presented a lesson appropriate to the time and the circumstances. Every neglect or insult shown by men to their fellowmen only made Him more conscious of their need of His divine-human sympathy. He sought to inspire with hope the roughest and most unpromising, setting before them the assurance that they might become blameless and harmless, attaining such a character as would make them manifest as the children of God.

Often He met those who had drifted under Satan's control, and who had no power to break from his snare. To such a one, discouraged, sick, tempted, fallen, Jesus would speak words of tenderest pity, words that were needed and could be understood. Others He met who were fighting a hand-to-hand battle with the adversary of souls. These He encouraged to persevere, assuring them that they would win; for angels of God were on their side, and would give them the victory.

At the table of the publicans He sat as an honored guest, by His sympathy and social kindliness showing that He recognized the dignity of humanity; and men longed to become worthy of His confidence. Upon their thirsty hearts His words fell with blessed, life-giving power. New impulses were awakened, and to these outcasts of society there opened the possibility of a new life.

Though He was a Jew, Jesus mingled freely with the Samaritans, setting at nought the Pharisaic customs of His nation. In face of their prejudices He accepted the hospitality of this despised people. He slept with them under their roofs, ate with them at their tables—partaking of the food prepared and served by their hands—taught in their streets, and treated them with the utmost kindness and courtesy. And while He drew their hearts to Him by the tie of human sympathy, His divine grace brought to them the salvation which the Jews rejected.

Salvation for All Races

Christ neglected no opportunity of proclaiming the gospel of salvation. Listen to His wonderful words to that one woman of Samaria. He was sitting by Jacob's well as the woman came to draw water. To her surprise He asked a favor of her. "Give Me to drink," He said. He wanted a cool draft, and He wished also to open the way whereby He might give her the water of life. "How is it," said the woman, "that Thou, being a Jew, askest drink of me, which am a woman of Samaria? for the Jews have no dealings with the Samaritans." Jesus answered, "If thou knewest the gift of God, and who it is that saith to thee, Give Me to drink; thou wouldest have asked of Him, and He would have given thee living water. . . . Whosoever drinketh of this water shall thirst again: but whosoever drinketh of the water that I shall give him shall never thirst; but the water that I shall give him shall be in him a well of water springing up into everlasting life." John 4:7-14.

How much interest Christ manifested in this one woman! How earnest and eloquent were His words! When the woman heard them, she left her waterpot, and went into the city, saying to her friends, "Come, see a man, which told me all things that ever I did: is not this the Christ?" We read that "many of the Samaritans of that city believed on Him." Verses 29, 39. And who can estimate the influence which these words have exerted for the saving of souls in the years that have passed since then?

Wherever hearts are open to receive the truth, Christ is ready to instruct them. He reveals to them the Father and the service acceptable to Him who reads the heart. For such He uses no parables. To them, as to the woman at the well, He says, "I that speak unto thee am He." Verse 26.

Ministry to the Sick and Needy

IN THE fisherman's home at Capernaum, the mother of Peter's wife is lying sick of "a great fever," and "they tell Him of her." Jesus "touched her hand, and the fever left her," and she arose and ministered to the Saviour and His disciples. Luke 4:38; Mark 1:30; Matthew 8:15.

Rapidly the tidings spread. The miracle had been wrought upon the Sabbath, and for fear of the rabbis the people dared not come for healing until the sun was set. Then from the homes, the shops, the marketplaces, the inhabitants of the city pressed toward the humble dwelling that sheltered Jesus. The sick were brought upon litters, they came leaning upon staves, or, supported by friends, they tottered feebly into the Saviour's presence.

Hour after hour they came and went; for none could know whether tomorrow would find the Healer still among them. Never before had Capernaum witnessed a day like this. The air was filled with the voice of triumph and shouts of deliverance.

Not until the last sufferer had been relieved did Jesus cease His work. It was far into the night when the multitude departed and silence settled down upon the home of Simon. The long, exciting day was past, and Jesus sought rest. But while the city was wrapped in slumber, the Sav-

173

iour, "rising up a great while before day, . . . went out, and departed into a solitary place, and there prayed." Mark 1:35.

"To Other Cities Also"

Early in the morning Peter and his companions came to Jesus, saying that already the people of Capernaum were seeking Him. With surprise they heard Christ's words, "I must preach the kingdom of God to other cities also: for therefore am I sent." Luke 4:43.

In the excitement which then pervaded Capernaum there was danger that the object of His mission would be lost sight of. Jesus was not satisfied to attract attention to Himself merely as a wonder-worker or as a healer of physical disease. He was seeking to draw men to Him as their Saviour. While the people were eager to believe that He had come as a king to establish an earthly reign, He desired to turn their minds from the earthly to the spiritual. Mere worldly success would interfere with His work.

And the wonder of the careless crowd jarred upon His spirits. No self-assertion mingled with His life. The homage which the world gives to position, wealth, or talent was foreign to the Son of man. None of the means that men employ to win allegiance or command homage did Jesus use. Centuries before His birth it had been prophesied of Him: "He shall not cry, nor lift up, nor cause His voice to be heard in the street. A bruised reed shall He not break, and the dimly burning flax shall He not quench: He shall bring forth judgment unto truth." Isaiah 42:2, 3, margin.

The Pharisees sought distinction by their scrupulous ceremonialism and the ostentation of their worship and their charities. They proved their zeal for religion by making it the theme of discussion. Disputes between opposing sects were loud and long, and it was not unusual to hear on the streets the voice of angry controversy from learned doctors of the law.

In marked contrast to all this was the life of Jesus. In that life no noisy disputation, no ostentatious worship, no act to gain applause, was ever witnessed. Christ was hid in God, and God was revealed in the character of His Son. To this revelation Jesus desired the minds of the people to be directed.

The Sun of Righteousness did not burst upon the world in splendor, to dazzle the senses with His glory. It is written of Christ, "His going forth is prepared as the morning." Hosea 6:3. Quietly and gently the daylight breaks upon the earth, dispelling the darkness and waking the world to life. So did the Sun of Righteousness arise, "with healing in His wings." Malachi 4:2.

"Behold My Servant, whom I uphold;
Mine Elect, in whom My soul delighteth."
Isaiah 42:1.

"Thou hast been a strength to the poor,
A strength to the needy in his distress,
A refuge from the storm, a shadow from the heat."
Isaiah 25:4.

"Art Thou He That Should Come?"

From Herod's dungeon, where, in disappointment and perplexity concerning the Saviour's work, John the Baptist watched and waited, he sent two of his disciples to Jesus with the message: "Art Thou He that should come, or do we look for another?" Matthew 11:3.

175

The Saviour did not at once answer the disciples' question. As they stood wondering at His silence, the afflicted were coming to Him. The voice of the Mighty Healer penetrated the deaf ear. A word, a touch of His hand, opened the blind eyes to behold the light of day, the scenes of nature, the faces of friends, and the face of the Deliverer. His voice reached the ears of the dying and they arose in health and vigor. Paralyzed demoniacs obeyed His word, their madness left them, and they worshiped Him. The poor peasants and laborers, who were shunned by the rabbis as unclean, gathered about Him, and He spoke to them the words of eternal life.

Thus the day wore away, the disciples of John seeing and hearing all. At last Jesus called them to Him, and bade them go and tell John what they had seen and heard, adding, "Blessed is he, whosoever shall not be offended in Me." Verse 6. The disciples bore the message, and it was enough.

John recalled the prophecy concerning the Messiah, "Jehovah hath anointed Me to preach good tidings unto the meek; He hath sent Me to bind up the broken hearted, to proclaim liberty to the captives, and the opening of the prison to them that are bound; to proclaim the year of Jehovah's favor, and . . . to comfort all that mourn." Isaiah 61:1, 2, A.R.V. Jesus of Nazareth was the Promised One. The evidence of His divinity was seen in His ministry to the needs of suffering humanity. His glory was shown in His condescension to our low estate.

The works of Christ not only declared Him to be the Messiah, but showed in what manner His kingdom was to be established. To John was opened the same truth that had come to Elijah in the desert, when "a great and strong wind rent the mountains, and brake in pieces the rocks before the Lord; but the Lord was not in the wind: and after the wind an earthquake; but the Lord was not in the earthquake: and after the earthquake a fire; but the Lord was not in the fire," and after the fire, God spoke to the prophet by a still small voice. 1 Kings 19:11, 12. So Jesus was to do His work, not by the overturning of thrones and kingdoms, not with pomp and outward display, but through speaking to the hearts of men by a life of mercy and self-sacrifice.

"Not With Outward Show"

The kingdom of God comes not with outward show. It comes through the gentleness of the inspiration of His Word, through the inward working of His Spirit, the fellowship of the soul with Him who is its life. The greatest manifestation of its power is seen in human nature brought to the perfection of the character of Christ.

The followers of Christ are to be the light of the world; but God does not bid them make an effort to shine. He does not approve of any self-satisfied endeavor to display superior goodness. He desires that their souls shall be imbued with the principles of heaven; then, as they come in contact with the world, they will reveal the light that is in them. Their steadfast fidelity in every act of life will be a means of illumination.

Wealth or high position, costly equipment, architecture, or furnishings, are not essential to the advancement of the work of God; neither are achievements that win applause from men and administer to vanity. Worldly display, however imposing, is of no value in God's sight. Above the seen and temporal, He values the unseen and eternal. The former is of worth only as it expresses the latter. The choicest productions of art possess no beauty that can compare with the beauty of character which is the fruit of the Holy Spirit's working in the soul.

When God gave His Son to our world, He endowed human beings with imperishable riches—riches compared with which the treasured wealth of men since the world began is nothingness. Christ came to the earth and stood before the children of men with the hoarded love of eternity, and this is the treasure that, through our connection with Him, we are to receive, to reveal, and to impart.

Human effort will be efficient in the work of God just according to the consecrated devotion of the worker—by revealing the power of the grace of Christ to transform the life. We are to be distinguished from the world because God has placed His seal upon us, because He manifests in us His own character of love. Our Redeemer covers us with His righteousness.

In choosing men and women for His service, God does not ask whether they possess worldly wealth, learning, or eloquence. He asks: Do they walk in such humility that I can teach them My way? Can I put My words into their lips? Will they represent Me?

God can use every person just in proportion as He can put His Spirit into the soul temple. The work that He will accept is the work that reflects His image. His followers are to bear as their credentials to the world the ineffaceable characteristics of His immortal principles.

As Jesus ministers in the streets of the cities, mothers with their sick and dying little ones in their arms press through the throng, seeking to come within reach of His notice.

"Suffer the Little Children"

Behold these mothers, pale, weary, almost despairing, yet determined and persevering. Bearing their burden of suffering, they seek the Saviour. As they are crowded back by the surging throng, Christ makes His way to them step by step, until He is close by their side. Hope springs up in their hearts. Their tears of gladness fall as they catch His attention, and look into the eyes expressing such pity and love.

Singling out one of the group, the Saviour invites her confidence, saying, "What shall I do for thee?" She sobs out her great want, "Master, that Thou wouldst heal my child." Christ takes the little one from her arms, and disease flees at His touch. The pallor of death is gone; the life-giving current flows through the veins; the muscles receive strength. Words of comfort and peace are spoken to the mother, and then another case, just as urgent, is presented. Again Christ exercises His life-giving power, and all give praise and honor to Him who doeth wonderful things.

We dwell much on the greatness of Christ's life. We speak of the wonderful things that He accomplished, of the miracles that He wrought. But His attention to things accounted small is even higher proof of His greatness.

Among the Jews it was customary for children to be brought to some rabbi, that he might lay his hands upon them in blessing; but the disciples thought the Saviour's work too important to be interrupted in this way. When the mothers came desiring Him to bless their little ones, the disciples looked on them with disfavor. They thought these children too young to be benefited by a visit to Jesus, and concluded that He would be displeased at their presence. But the Saviour understood the care and burden of the mothers who were seeking to train their children according to the Word of God. He had heard their prayers. He Himself had drawn them into His presence.

One mother with her child had left her home to find Jesus. On the way she told a neighbor her errand, and the neighbor wished to have Jesus bless her children. Thus several mothers came here together, with their little ones. Some of the children had passed beyond the years of infancy to childhood and youth. When the mothers made known their desire, Jesus heard with sympathy the timid, tearful request. But He waited to see how the disciples would treat them. When He saw the disciples reproving the mothers and sending them away, thinking to do Him a favor, He showed them their error, saying, "Suffer the little children to come unto Me, and forbid them not: for of such is the kingdom of God." Mark 10:14. He took the children in His arms, He laid His hands upon them, and gave them the blessings for which they came.

The mothers were comforted. They returned to their homes strengthened and blessed by the words of Christ. They were encouraged to take up their burden with new cheerfulness, and to work hopefully for their children.

Could the afterlife of that little group be opened before us, we should see the mothers recalling to the minds of their children the scene of that day, and repeating to them the loving words of the Saviour. We should see, too, how often, in afteryears, the memory of these words kept the children from straying from the path cast up for the ransomed of the Lord.

The Helper of Mothers

Christ is today the same compassionate Saviour as when He walked among men. He is as verily the helper of mothers now as when He gathered the little ones to His arms in Judea. The children of our hearths are as much the purchase of His blood as were the children of long ago.

Jesus knows the burden of every mother's heart. He who had a mother that struggled with poverty and privation, sympathizes with every mother in her labors. He who made a long journey in order to relieve the anxious heart of a Canaanite woman will do as much for the mothers of today. He who gave back to the widow of Nain her only son, and in His agony upon the cross remembered His own mother, is touched today by the mother's sorrow. In every grief and every need He will comfort and help.

Let mothers come to Jesus with their perplexities. They will find grace sufficient to aid them in the care of their children. The gates are open for every mother who would lay her burdens at the Saviour's feet. He who said, "Suffer the little children to come unto Me, and forbid them not" (Mark 10:14), still invites mothers to bring their little ones to be blessed by Him.

In the children who were brought in contact with Him, Jesus saw the men and women who should be heirs of His grace and subjects of His kingdom, and some of whom would become martyrs for His sake. He knew that these children would listen to Him and accept Him as their Redeemer far more readily than would grown-up people, many of whom were the worldly-wise and hardhearted. In teaching, He came down to their level. He, the Majesty of heaven, an-

181

swered their questions and simplified His important lessons to meet their childish understanding. He planted in their minds the seeds of truth, which in afteryears would spring up and bear fruit unto eternal life.

When Jesus told the disciples not to forbid the children to come to Him, He was speaking to His followers in all ages—to officers of the church, ministers, helpers, and all Christians. Jesus is drawing the children, and He bids us, "Suffer them to come;" as if He would say, They will come, if you do not hinder them.

Let not your un-Christlike character misrepresent Jesus. Do not keep the little ones away from Him by your coldness and harshness. Never give them cause to feel that heaven would not be a pleasant place to them if you were there. Do not speak of religion as something that children cannot understand, or act as if they were not expected to accept Christ in their childhood. Do not give them the false impression that the religion of Christ is a religion of gloom, and that in coming to the Saviour they must give up all that makes life joyful.

As the Holy Spirit moves upon the hearts of the children, cooperate with His work. Teach them that the Saviour is calling them, that nothing can afford Him greater joy than for them to give themselves to Him in the bloom and freshness of their years.

The Saviour regards with infinite tenderness the souls whom He has purchased with His blood. They are the claim of His love. He looks upon them with unutterable longing. His heart is drawn out, not only to the best-trained and most attractive children, but to those who by inheritance and through neglect have objectionable traits of char-

182

acter. Many parents do not understand how much they are responsible for these traits in their children. They have not the tenderness and wisdom to deal with the erring ones whom they have made what they are. But Jesus looks upon these children with pity. He traces from cause to effect.

The Christian worker may be Christ's agent in drawing these faulty and erring ones to the Saviour. By wisdom and tact he may bind them to his heart, he may give courage and hope, and through the grace of Christ may see them transformed in character, so that of them it may be said, "Of such is the kingdom of God."

"Give Ye Them to Eat"

All day the people had thronged the steps of Christ and His disciples as He taught beside the sea. They had listened to His gracious words, so simple and so plain that they were as the balm of Gilead to their souls. The healing of His divine hand had brought health to the sick and life to the dying. The day had seemed to them like heaven on earth, and they were unconscious of how long it had been since they had eaten anything.

The sun was sinking in the west, and yet the people lingered. Finally the disciples came to Christ, urging that for their own sake the multitude should be sent away. Many had come from far, and had eaten nothing since morning. In the surrounding towns and villages they might be able to obtain food. But Jesus said, "Give ye them to eat." Matthew 14:16. Then, turning to Philip, He questioned, "Whence shall we buy bread, that these may eat?" John 6:5.

Philip looked over the sea of heads, and thought how impossible it would be to provide food for so great a company. He answered that two hundred pennyworth of bread would not be enough to divide among them, so that each might have a little.

Jesus inquired how much food could be found among the company. "There is a lad here," said Andrew, "which hath five barley loaves, and two small fishes: but what are they among so many?" Verse 9. Jesus directed that these be brought to Him. Then He bade the disciples seat the people on the grass. When this was accomplished, He took the food, "and looking up to heaven, He blessed, and brake, and gave the loaves to His disciples, and the disciples to the multitude. And they did all eat, and were filled: and they took up of the fragments that remained twelve baskets full." Matthew 14:19, 20.

Humble Fare Provided

It was by a miracle of divine power that Christ fed the multitude; yet how humble was the fare provided—only the fishes and barley loaves that were the daily fare of the fisherfolk of Galilee.

Christ could have spread for the people a rich repast, but food prepared merely for the gratification of appetite would have conveyed no lesson for their good. Through this miracle Christ desired to teach a lesson of simplicity.

If men today were simple in their habits, living in harmony with nature's law, as did Adam and Eve in the beginning, there would be an abundant supply for the needs of the human family. But selfishness and the indulgence of appetite have brought sin and misery, from excess on the one hand, and from want on the other.

Jesus did not seek to attract the people to Him by grati-

184

fying the desire for luxury. To that great throng, weary and hungry after the long, exciting day, the simple fare was an assurance both of His power and of His tender care for them in the common needs of life. The Saviour has not promised His followers the luxuries of the world; their lot may be shut in by poverty; but His word is pledged that their need shall be supplied, and He has promised that which is better than earthly good—the abiding comfort of His own presence.

After the multitude had been fed, there was an abundance of food left. Jesus bade His disciples, "Gather up the fragments that remain, that nothing be lost." John 6:12. These words meant more than putting the food into baskets. The lesson was twofold. Nothing is to be wasted. We are to let slip no temporal advantage. We should neglect nothing that would serve to benefit a human being. Let everything be gathered up that will relieve the necessities of earth's hungry ones. With the same carefulness are we to treasure the bread from heaven to satisfy the needs of the soul. By every word of God we are to live. Nothing that God has spoken is to be lost. Not one word that concerns our eternal salvation are we to neglect. Not one word is to fall useless to the ground.

Dependence Upon God

The miracle of the loaves teaches dependence upon God. When Christ fed the five thousand, the food was not nigh at hand. Apparently He had no means at His command. There He was, with five thousand men, besides women and children, in the wilderness. He had not invited the multitude to follow Him thither. Eager to be in His presence, they had come without invitation or command; but He knew that after listening all day to His instruction they were hungry and faint. They were far from home, and the night was at hand. Many of them were without means to purchase food. He who for their sake had fasted forty days in the wilderness would not suffer them to return fasting to their homes.

The providence of God had placed Jesus where He was; and He depended on His heavenly Father for means to relieve the necessity. When we are brought into strait places, we are to depend on God. In every emergency we are to seek help from Him who has infinite resources at His command.

In this miracle, Christ received from the Father; He imparted to the disciples, the disciples to the people, and the people to one another. So all who are united to Christ will receive from Him the bread of life, and impart it to others. His disciples are the appointed means of communication between Christ and the people.

Christ Will Multiply the Gift

When the disciples heard the Saviour's direction, "Give ye them to eat," all the difficulties arose in their minds. They questioned, Shall we go into the villages to buy food? But what said Christ? "Give *ye* them to eat." The disciples brought to Jesus all they had; but He did not invite them to eat. He bade them serve the people. The food multiplied in His hands; and the hands of the disciples, reaching out to Christ, were never unfilled. The little store was sufficient for all. When the multitude had been fed, the disciples ate with Jesus of the precious, heaven-supplied food.

As we see the necessities of the poor, the ignorant, the afflicted, how often our hearts sink. We question: What avail our feeble strength and slender resources to supply this terrible necessity? Shall we not wait for someone of greater ability to direct the work, or for some organization to undertake it? Christ says, "Give *ye* them to eat." Use the means, the time, the ability, you have. Bring your barley loaves to Jesus.

Though your resources may not be sufficient to feed thousands, they may suffice to feed one. In the hand of Christ they may feed many. Like the disciples, give what you have. Christ will multiply the gift. He will reward honest, simple reliance upon Him. That which seemed but a meager supply will prove to be a rich feast.

"He that soweth sparingly shall reap also sparingly; and he that soweth with blessings shall reap also with blessings. . . . God is able to make all grace abound unto you; that ye, having always all sufficiency in everything, may abound unto every good work: as it is written,

"He hath scattered abroad, He hath given to the poor;
His righteousness abideth forever.

"And He that supplieth seed to the sower and bread for food, shall supply and multiply your seed for sowing, and increase the fruits of your righteousness:.ye being enriched in everything unto all liberality." 2 Corinthians 9:6-11, R.V., margin.

With Nature and With God

THE Saviour's life on earth was a life of communion with nature and with God. In this communion He revealed for us the secret of a life of power.

Jesus was an earnest, constant worker. Never lived there among men another so weighted with responsibilities. Never another carried so heavy a burden of the world's sorrow and sin. Never another toiled with such self-consuming zeal for the good of men. Yet His was a life of health. Physically as well as spiritually He was represented by the sacrificial lamb, "without blemish and without spot." 1 Peter 1:19. In body as in soul He was an example of what God designed all humanity to be through obedience to His laws.

As the people looked upon Jesus, they saw a face in which divine compassion was blended with conscious power. He seemed to be surrounded with an atmosphere of spiritual life. While His manners were gentle and unassuming, He impressed men with a sense of power that was hidden, yet could not be wholly concealed.

During His ministry He was continually pursued by crafty and hypocritical men who were seeking His life. Spies were on His track, watching His words, to find some occasion against Him. The keenest and most highly cultured minds of the nation sought to defeat Him in controversy. But never could they gain an advantage. They had to retire from the field, confounded and put to shame by the lowly Teacher from Galilee. Christ's teaching had a freshness and a power such as men had never before known. Even His enemies were forced to confess, "Never man spake like this Man." John 7:46.

Understanding Nature's Mysteries

The childhood of Jesus, spent in poverty, had been uncorrupted by the artificial habits of a corrupt age. Working at the carpenter's bench, bearing the burdens of homelife, learning the lessons of obedience and toil, He found recreation amidst the scenes of nature, gathering knowledge as He sought to understand nature's mysteries. He studied the Word of God, and His hours of greatest happiness were found when He could turn aside from the scene of His labors to go into the fields, to meditate in the quiet valleys, to hold communion with God on the mountainside or amid the trees of the forest. The early morning often found Him in some secluded place, meditating, searching the Scriptures, or in prayer. With the voice of singing He welcomed the morning light. With songs of thanksgiving He cheered His hours of labor, and brought heaven's gladness to the toilworn and disheartened.

During His ministry Jesus lived to a great degree an outdoor life. His journeys from place to place were made on foot, and much of His teaching was given in the open air. In training His disciples He often withdrew from the confusion of the city to the quiet of the fields, as more in harmony with the lessons of simplicity, faith, and self-abnegation He desired to teach them. It was beneath the sheltering trees of the mountainside, but a little distance from the Sea of Galilee, that the Twelve were called to the apostolate and the Sermon on the Mount was given.

Christ loved to gather the people about Him under the blue heavens, on some grassy hillside, or on the beach beside the lake. Here, surrounded by the works of His own creation, He could turn their thoughts from the artificial to the natural. In the growth and development of nature were revealed the principles of His kingdom. As men should lift their eyes to the hills of God, and behold the wonderful works of His hand, they could learn precious lessons of divine truth. In future days the lessons of the divine Teacher would thus be repeated to them by the things of nature. The mind would be uplifted and the heart would find rest.

Communion With the Father

The disciples who were associated with Him in His work, Jesus often released for a season, that they might visit their homes and rest; but in vain were their efforts to draw Him away from His labors. All day He ministered to the throngs that came to Him, and at eventide, or in the early morning, He went away to the sanctuary of the mountains for communion with His Father.

Often His incessant labor and the conflict with the enmity and false teaching of the rabbis, left Him so utterly wearied that His mother and brothers, and even His disciples, feared that His life would be sacrificed. But as He returned from the hours of prayer that closed the toilsome day, they marked the look of peace upon His face, the freshness and life and power that seemed to pervade His whole being. From hours spent alone with God He came forth, morning by morning, to bring the light of heaven to men.

It was just after the return from their first missionary tour that Jesus bade His disciples, Come apart, and rest awhile. The disciples had returned, filled with the joy of their success as heralds of the gospel, when the tidings reached them of the death of John the Baptist at the hand of Herod. It was a bitter sorrow and disappointment. Jesus knew that in leaving the Baptist to die in prison He had severely tested the disciples' faith. With pitying tenderness He looked upon their sorrowful, tear-stained faces. Tears were in His own eyes and voice as He said, "Come ye yourselves apart into a desert place, and rest awhile." Mark 6:31.

Near Bethsaida, at the northern end of the Sea of Galilee, was a lonely region, beautiful with the fresh green of spring, that offered a welcome retreat to Jesus and His disciples. For this place they set out, going in their boat across the lake. Here they could rest, apart from the confusion of the multitude. Here the disciples could listen to the words of Christ, undisturbed by the retorts and accusations of the Pharisees. Here they hoped to enjoy a short season of fellowship in the society of their Lord.

Only a short time did Jesus have alone with His beloved ones, but how precious to them were those few moments. They talked together regarding the work of the gospel and the possibility of making their labor more effective in reaching the people. As Jesus opened to them the treasures of truth, they were vitalized by divine power and inspired with hope and courage.

But soon He was again sought for by the multitude. Supposing that He had gone to His usual place of retirement, the people followed Him thither. His hope to gain even one hour of rest was frustrated. But in the depths of His pure, compassionate heart, the Good Shepherd of the sheep had only love and pity for these restless, thirsting souls. All day He ministered to their needs, and at evening dismissed them to go to their homes and rest.

In a life wholly devoted to the good of others, the Saviour found it necessary to turn aside from ceaseless activity and contact with human needs, to seek retirement and unbroken communion with His Father. As the throng that had followed Him depart, He goes into the mountains, and there, alone with God, pours out His soul in prayer for these suffering, sinful, needy ones.

"Come . . . and Rest Awhile"

When Jesus said to His disciples that the harvest was great and the laborers were few, He did not urge upon them the necessity of ceaseless toil, but bade them, "Pray ye therefore the Lord of the harvest, that He will send forth laborers into His harvest." Matthew 9:38. To His toilworn workers today as really as to His first disciples He speaks these words of compassion, "Come ye yourselves apart, . . . and rest awhile."

All who are under the training of God need the quiet hour for communion with their own hearts, with nature, and with God. In them is to be revealed a life that is not in harmony with the world, its customs, or its practices; and they need to have a personal experience in obtaining a knowledge of the will of God. We must individually hear Him speaking to the heart. When every other voice is hushed, and in quietness we wait before Him, the silence of the soul makes more distinct the voice of God. He bids us, "Be still, and know that I am God." Psalm 46:10. This is the effectual preparation for all labor for God. Amidst the hurrying throng and the strain of life's intense activities, he who is thus refreshed will be surrounded with an atmosphere of light and peace. He will receive a new endowment of both physical and mental strength. His life will breathe out a fragrance, and will reveal a divine power that will reach men's hearts.

Adventures in Faith

"IF I MAY but touch His garment, I shall be whole." Matthew 9:21. It was a poor woman who spoke these words—a woman who for twelve years had suffered from a disease that made her life a burden. She had spent all her means upon physicians and remedies, only to be pronounced incurable. But as she heard of the Great Healer, her hopes revived. She thought, If only I could get near enough to speak to Him, I might be healed.

Christ was on His way to the home of Jairus, the Jewish rabbi who had entreated Him to come and heal his daughter. The heartbroken petition, "My little daughter lieth at the point of death: I pray Thee, come and lay Thy hands on her, that she may be healed" (Mark 5:23), had touched the tender, sympathetic heart of Christ, and He at once set out with the ruler for his home.

They advanced but slowly, for the crowd pressed Christ on every side. In making His way through the multitude, the Saviour came near to where the afflicted woman was standing. Again and again she had tried in vain to get near Him. Now her opportunity had come. She could see no way of speaking to Him. She would not seek to hinder His slow advance. But she had heard that healing came from a touch of His garments; and, fearful of losing her one

194

chance for relief, she pressed forward, saying to herself, "If I may but touch His garment, I shall be whole."

Christ knew every thought of her mind, and He was making His way to where she stood. He realized her great need, and He was helping her to exercise faith.

As He was passing, she reached forward and succeeded in barely touching the border of His garment. That moment she knew that she was healed. In that one touch was concentrated the faith of her life, and instantly her pain and feebleness disappeared. Instantly she felt the thrill as of an electric current passing through every fiber of her being. There came over her a sensation of perfect health. "She felt in her body that she was healed of that plague." Mark 5:29.

"Who Touched Me?"

The grateful woman desired to express her thanks to the Mighty Healer, who had done more for her in one touch than the physicians had done in twelve long years; but she dared not. With a grateful heart she tried to withdraw from the crowd. Suddenly Jesus stopped, and looking round He asked, "Who touched Me?"

Looking at Him in amazement, Peter answered, "Master, the multitude throng Thee and press Thee, and sayest Thou, Who touched Me?" Luke 8:45.

"Somebody hath touched Me," Jesus said; "for I perceive that virtue is gone out of Me." Verse 46. He could distinguish the touch of faith from the casual touch of the careless throng. Someone had touched Him with a deep purpose, and had received answer.

Christ did not ask the question for His own information.

195

He had a lesson for the people, for His disciples, and for the woman. He wished to inspire the afflicted with hope. He wished to show that it was faith which had brought the healing power. The woman's trust must not be passed by without comment. God must be glorified by her grateful confession. Christ desired her to understand that He approved her act of faith. He would not have her depart with a half blessing only. She was not to remain in ignorance of His knowledge of her suffering, or of His compassionate love and of His approval of her faith in His power to save to the uttermost all who come to Him.

Looking toward the woman, Christ insisted on knowing who had touched Him. Finding concealment vain, she came forward trembling, and cast herself at His feet. With grateful tears she told Him, before all the people, why she had touched His garment, and how she had been immediately healed. She feared that her act in touching His garment had been one of presumption; but no word of censure came from Christ's lips. He spoke only words of approval. They came from a heart of love, filled with sympathy for human woe. "Daughter," He said gently, "be of good comfort: thy faith hath made thee whole; go in peace." Verse 48. How cheering were these words to her. Now no fear that she had given offense embittered her joy.

The Touch of Faith

To the curious crowd pressing about Jesus there was imparted no vital power. But the suffering woman who touched Him in faith received healing. So in spiritual things does the casual contact differ from the touch of faith. To believe in Christ merely as the Saviour of the world can

196

never bring healing to the soul. The faith that is unto salvation is not a mere assent to the truth of the gospel. True faith is that which receives Christ as a personal Saviour. God gave His only-begotten Son, that *I*, by believing in Him, "should not perish, but have everlasting life." John 3:16. When I come to Christ, according to His word, I am to believe that I receive His saving grace. The life that I now live, I am to "live by the faith of the Son of God, who loved *me*, and gave Himself for *me*." Galatians 2:20.

Many hold faith as an opinion. Saving faith is a transaction, by which those who receive Christ join themselves in covenant relation with God. A living faith means an increase of vigor, a confiding trust, by which, through the grace of Christ, the soul becomes a conquering power.

Faith is a mightier conqueror than death. If the sick can be led to fix their eyes in faith upon the Mighty Healer, we shall see wonderful results. It will bring life to the body and to the soul.

In working for the victims of evil habits, instead of pointing them to the despair and ruin toward which they are hastening, turn their eyes away to Jesus. Fix them upon the glories of the heavenly. This will do more for the saving of body and soul than will all the terrors of the grave when kept before the helpless and apparently hopeless.

Healing the Centurion's Servant

A centurion's servant was lying sick of the palsy. Among the Romans the servants were slaves, bought and sold in the marketplaces, and often treated with abuse and cruelty; but the centurion was tenderly attached to his servant, and greatly desired his recovery. He believed that Jesus could heal him. He had not seen the Saviour, but the reports he had heard inspired him with faith. Notwithstanding the formalism of the Jews, this Roman was convinced that their religion was superior to his own. Already he had broken through the barriers of national prejudice and hatred that separated the conquerors from the conquered people. He had manifested respect for the service of God, and had shown kindness to the Jews as His worshipers. In the teaching of Christ, as it had been reported to him, he found that which met the need of the soul. All that was spiritual within him responded to the Saviour's words. But he thought himself unworthy to approach Jesus, and he appealed to the Jewish elders to make request for his servant's healing.

The elders present the case to Jesus, urging that "he was worthy for whom He should do this: for he loveth our nation, and he hath built us a synagogue." Luke 7:4, 5.

But on the way to the centurion's home, Jesus receives a message from the officer himself, "Lord, trouble not Thyself: for I am not worthy that Thou shouldest enter under my roof." Verse 6.

"Speak the Word Only"

Still the Saviour keeps on His way, and the centurion comes in person to complete the message, saying, "Neither thought I myself worthy to come unto Thee," "but speak the word only, and my servant shall be healed. For I am a man under authority, having soldiers under me: and I say to this man, Go, and he goeth; and to another, Come, and he cometh; and to my servant, Do this, and he doeth it." Verse 7; Matthew 8:8, 9.

I represent the power of Rome, and my soldiers recognize

my authority as supreme. So dost Thou represent the power of the infinite God, and all created things obey Thy word. Thou canst command the disease to depart, and it shall obey Thee. Speak but the word, and my servant shall be healed.

"As thou hast believed," Christ said, "so be it done unto thee. And his servant was healed in the selfsame hour." Verse 13.

The Jewish elders had commended the centurion to Christ because of the favor he had shown to "our nation." "He was worthy," they said, for "he hath built us a synagogue." But the centurion said of himself, "I am not worthy." Luke 7:4-6. Yet he did not fear to ask help from Jesus. Not to his own goodness did he trust, but to the Saviour's mercy. His only argument was his great need.

In the same way every human being can come to Christ. "Not by works of righteousness which we have done, but according to His mercy He saved us." Titus 3:5. Do you feel that, because you are a sinner, you cannot hope to receive blessing from God? Remember that Christ came into the world to save sinners. We have nothing to recommend us to God; the plea that we may urge now and ever is our utterly helpless condition, which makes His redeeming power a necessity. Renouncing all self-dependence, we may look to the cross of Calvary and say—

> "In my hand no price I bring;
> Simply to Thy cross I cling."

"If thou canst believe, all things are possible to him that believeth." Mark 9:23. It is faith that connects us with heaven and brings us strength for coping with the powers of darkness. In Christ, God has provided means for subduing every evil trait and resisting every temptation, however strong. But many feel that they lack faith, and therefore they remain away from Christ. Let these souls, in their helpless unworthiness, cast themselves upon the mercy of their compassionate Saviour. Look not to self, but to Christ. He who healed the sick and cast out demons when He walked among men is still the same mighty Redeemer. Then grasp His promises as leaves from the tree of life: "Him that cometh to Me I will in no wise cast out." John 6:37.

The Leper Cleansed

Of all the diseases known in the East the leprosy was most dreaded. Its incurable and contagious character, and its horrible effect upon its victims, filled the bravest with fear. Among the Jews it was regarded as a judgment on account of sin, and hence was called "the stroke," "the finger of God." Deep-rooted, ineradicable, deadly, it was looked upon as a symbol of sin.

By the ritual law the leper was pronounced unclean. Whatever he touched was unclean. The air was polluted by his breath. Like one already dead, he was shut out from the habitations of men. One who was suspected of having the disease must present himself to the priests, who were to examine and decide his case. If pronounced a leper, he was isolated from his family, cut off from the congregation of Israel, and doomed to associate with those only who were similarly afflicted. Even kings and rulers were not exempt. A monarch attacked by this terrible disease must yield up the scepter and flee from society.

Away from his friends and his kindred, the leper must bear the curse of his malady. He was obliged to publish his own calamity, to rend his garments, and to sound the alarm, warning all to flee from his contaminating presence. The cry, "Unclean! unclean!" coming in mournful tones from the lonely exile, was a signal heard with fear and abhorrence.

In the region of Christ's ministry were many of these sufferers, and as the news of His work reached them, there is one in whose heart faith begins to spring up. If he could go to Jesus, he might be healed. But how can he find Jesus? Doomed as he is to perpetual isolation, how can he present himself to the Healer? And will Christ heal him? Will He not, like the Pharisees, and even the physicians, pronounce a curse upon him, and warn him to flee from the haunts of men?

Not One Has Been Turned Away

He thinks of all that has been told him of Jesus. Not one who has sought His help has been turned away. The wretched man determines to find the Saviour. Though shut out from the cities, it may be that he can cross His path in some byway along the mountain roads, or find Him as He is teaching outside the towns. The difficulties are great, but this is his only hope.

Standing afar off, the leper catches a few words from the Saviour's lips. He sees Him laying His hands upon the sick. He sees the lame, the blind, the paralytic, and those dying of various maladies, rise up in health, praising God for deliverance. His faith strengthens. Nearer and yet nearer he approaches to the listening throng. The restrictions laid upon him, the safety of the people, the fear with which all men regard him, are alike forgotten. He thinks only of the blessed hope of healing.

"Thou Canst Make Me Clean"

He is a loathsome spectacle. The disease has made frightful inroads, and his decaying body is horrible to look upon. At sight of him the people fall back. In their terror they crowd upon one another to escape from contact with him. Some try to prevent him from approaching Jesus, but in vain. He neither sees nor hears them. Their expressions of loathing are lost upon him. He sees only the Son of God, he hears only the voice that speaks life to the dying.

Pressing to Jesus, he casts himself at His feet with the cry, "Lord, if Thou wilt, Thou canst make me clean." Matthew 8:2.

Jesus replies, "I will; be thou clean," and lays His hand upon him. Verse 3.

Immediately a change passes over the leper. His blood becomes healthy, the nerves sensitive, the muscles firm. The unnaturally white, scaly surface peculiar to leprosy disappears; and his flesh becomes as the flesh of a little child.

Should the priests learn the facts concerning the healing of the leper, their hatred of Christ might lead them to render a dishonest sentence. Jesus desired that an impartial decision be secured. He therefore bids the man tell no one of the cure, but without delay present himself at the temple with an offering before any rumors concerning the miracle should be spread abroad.

Before the priests could accept such an offering, they were required to examine the offerer and certify his complete recovery.

This examination was made. The priests who had condemned the leper to banishment testified to his cure. The healed man was restored to his home and society. He felt that the boon of health was very precious. He rejoiced in the vigor of manhood, and in his restoration to his family. Notwithstanding the caution of Jesus, he could no longer conceal the fact of his cure, and joyfully he went about proclaiming the power of the One who had made him whole.

When this man came to Jesus, he was "full of leprosy." Its deadly poison permeated his whole body. The disciples sought to prevent their Master from touching him; for he who touched a leper became himself unclean. But in laying His hand upon the leper, Jesus received no defilement. The leprosy was cleansed. Thus it is with the leprosy of sin— deep-rooted, deadly, impossible to be cleansed by human power. "The whole head is sick, and the whole heart faint. From the sole of the foot even unto the head there is no soundness in it; but wounds, and bruises, and putrefying sores." Isaiah 1:5, 6. But Jesus, coming to dwell in humanity, receives no pollution. His presence was healing virtue for the sinner. Whoever will fall at His feet, saying in faith, "Lord, if Thou wilt, Thou canst make me clean," shall hear the answer, "I will; be thou clean."

In some instances of healing, Jesus did not at once grant the blessing sought. But in the case of leprosy, no sooner was the appeal made than it was granted. When we pray for earthly blessings, the answer to our prayer may be delayed, or God may give us something other than we ask; but not so when we ask for deliverance from sin. It is His will to cleanse us from sin, to make us His children, and to enable us to live a holy life. Christ "gave Himself for our sins, that He might deliver us from this present evil world, according to the will of God and our Father." "And this is the confidence that we have in Him, that, if we ask anything according to His will, He heareth us: and if we know that He hear us, whatsoever we ask, we know that we have the petitions that we desired of Him." Galations 1:4; 1 John 5:14, 15.

Jesus looked upon the distressed and heart-burdened, those whose hopes were blighted, and who with earthly joys were seeking to quiet the longing of the soul, and He invited all to find rest in Him.

Tenderly He bade the toiling people, "Take My yoke upon you, and learn of Me; for I am meek and lowly in heart: and ye shall find rest unto your souls." Matthew 11:29.

Christ Speaks to All

In these words, Christ was speaking to every human being. Whether they know it or not, all are weary and heavy-laden. All are weighed down with burdens that only Christ can remove. The heaviest burden that we bear is the burden of sin. If we were left to bear this burden, it would crush us. But the Sinless One has taken our place. "The Lord hath laid on Him the iniquity of us all." Isaiah 53:6.

He has borne the burden of our guilt. He will take the load from our weary shoulders. He will give us rest. The burden of care and sorrow also He will bear. He invites us to cast all our care upon Him; for He carries us upon His heart.

The Elder Brother of our race is by the eternal throne. He looks upon every soul who is turning his face toward Him as the Saviour. He knows by experience what are the weaknesses of humanity, what are our wants, and where lies the strength of our temptations; for He was "in all points tempted like as we are, yet without sin." Hebrews 4:15. He is watching over you, trembling child of God. Are you tempted? He will deliver. Are you weak? He will strengthen. Are you ignorant? He will enlighten. Are you wounded? He will heal. The Lord "telleth the number of the stars;" and yet "He healeth the broken in heart, and bindeth up their wounds." Psalm 147:4, 3.

Greater than the love of a mother for her child is Christ's love for His redeemed. It is our privilege to rest in His love; to say, "I will trust Him; for He gave His life for me."

Human love may change; but Christ's love knows no change. When we cry to Him for help, His hand is stretched out to save.

205

Healing the Soul

MANY of those who came to Christ for help had brought disease upon themselves; yet He did not refuse to heal them. And when virtue from Him entered into these souls, they were convicted of sin, and many were healed of their spiritual disease as well as of their physical maladies.

Among these was the paralytic at Capernaum. Like the leper, this paralytic had lost all hope of recovery. His disease was the result of a sinful life, and his sufferings were embittered by remorse. In vain he had appealed to the Pharisees and doctors for relief; they pronounced him incurable, they denounced him as a sinner, and declared that he would die under the wrath of God.

The palsied man had sunk into despair. Then he heard of the works of Jesus. Others as sinful and helpless as he had been healed, and he was encouraged to believe that he, too, might be cured if he could be carried to the Saviour. But hope fell as he remembered the cause of his malady, yet he could not cast away the possibility of healing.

His great desire was relief from the burden of sin. He longed to see Jesus, and receive the assurance of forgiveness and peace with Heaven. Then he would be content to live or to die, according to God's will.

There was no time to lose; already his wasted flesh bore signs of death. He besought his friends to carry him on his bed to Jesus, and this they gladly undertook to do. But so dense was the crowd that had assembled in and about the house where the Saviour was that it was impossible for the sick man and his friends to reach Him or even to come within hearing of His voice. Jesus was teaching in the home of Peter. According to their custom, His disciples sat close about Him, "and there were Pharisees and doctors of the law sitting by, who were come out of every village of Galilee and Judea and Jerusalem." Luke 5:17, A.R.V. Many of these had come as spies, seeking an accusation against Jesus. Beyond these thronged the promiscuous multitude, the eager, the reverent, the curious, and the unbelieving. Different nationalities and all grades of society were represented. "And the power of the Lord was present to heal them." Luke 5:17. The Spirit of life brooded over the assembly, but Pharisees and doctors did not discern His presence. They felt no sense of need, and the healing was not for them. "He hath filled the hungry with good things; and the rich He hath sent empty away." Luke 1:53.

At the Feet of Jesus

Again and again the bearers of the paralytic tried to push their way through the crowd, but in vain. The sick man looked about him in unutterable anguish. How could he relinquish hope, when the longed-for help was so near? At his suggestion his friends bore him to the top of the house, and, breaking up the roof, let him down at the feet of Jesus.

The discourse was interrupted. The Saviour looked upon the mournful countenance and saw the pleading eyes fixed upon Him. Well He knew the longing of that burdened soul. It was Christ who had brought conviction to his conscience when he was yet at home. When he repented of his sins, and believed in the power of Jesus to make him whole, the mercy of the Saviour had blessed his heart. Jesus had watched the first glimmer of faith grow into a conviction that He was the sinner's only helper, and had seen it grow stronger with every effort to come into His presence. It was Christ who had drawn the sufferer to Himself. Now, in words that fell like music on the listener's ear, the Saviour said, "Son, be of good cheer; thy sins be forgiven thee." Matthew 9:2.

Burden of Guilt Removed

The burden of guilt rolls from the sick man's soul. He cannot doubt. Christ's words reveal His power to read the heart. Who can deny His power to forgive sins? Hope takes the place of despair; and joy, of oppressive gloom. The man's physical pain is gone, and his whole being is transformed. Making no further request, he lay in peaceful silence, too happy for words.

Many were watching with breathless interest every movement in this strange transaction. Many felt that Christ's words were an invitation to them. Were they not soul-sick because of sin? Were they not anxious to be freed from this burden?

But the Pharisees, fearful of losing their influence with the multitude, said in their hearts, "He blasphemeth: who can forgive sins but One, even God?" Mark 2:7, R.V.

Fixing His glance upon them, beneath which they cowered and drew back, Jesus said, "Wherefore think ye evil in your hearts? For whether is easier, to say, Thy sins be forgiven thee; or to say, Arise, and walk? But that ye may know that the Son of man hath power on earth to forgive sins," He said, turning to the paralytic, "Arise, take up thy bed, and go unto thine house." Matthew 9:4-6.

Then he who had been borne on a litter to Jesus rose to his feet with the elasticity and strength of youth. And immediately he "took up the bed, and went forth before them all; insomuch that they were all amazed, and glorified God, saying, We never saw it on this fashion." Mark 2:12.

Creative Power

It required nothing less than creative power to restore health to that decaying body. The same voice that spoke life to man created from the dust of the earth, had spoken life to the dying paralytic. And the same power that gave life to the body had renewed the heart. He who at creation "spake, and it was," who "commanded, and it stood fast" (Psalm 33:9), had spoken life to the soul dead in trespasses and sins. The healing of the body was an evidence of the power that had renewed the heart. Christ bade the paralytic arise and walk, "that ye may know," He said, "that the Son of man hath power on earth to forgive sins."

The paralytic found in Christ healing for both the soul and the body. He needed health of soul before he could appreciate health of body. Before the physical malady could be healed, Christ must bring relief to the mind, and cleanse the soul from sin. This lesson should not be overlooked. There are today thousands suffering from physical disease who, like the paralytic, are longing for the message, "Thy sins are forgiven." The burden of sin, with its unrest and

209

unsatisfied desires, is the foundation of their maladies. They can find no relief until they come to the Healer of the soul. The peace which He alone can impart would restore vigor to the mind and health to the body.

Heaven's Gates Opened

The effect produced upon the people by the healing of the paralytic was as if heaven had opened and revealed the glories of the better world. As the man who had been cured passed through the throng, blessing God at every step, and bearing his burden as if it were a feather's weight, the people fell back to give him room, and with awestricken faces gazed upon him, whispering softly among themselves, "We have seen strange things today." Luke 5:26.

In the home of the paralytic there was great rejoicing when he returned to his family, carrying with ease the couch upon which he had been slowly borne from their presence but a short time before. They gathered round with tears of joy, hardly daring to believe their eyes. He stood before them in the full vigor of manhood. Those arms that they had seen lifeless were quick to obey his will. The flesh that had been shrunken and leaden-hued was now fresh and ruddy. He walked with a firm, free step. Joy and hope were written in every lineament of his countenance; and an expression of purity and peace had taken the place of the marks of sin and suffering. Glad thanksgiving went up from that home, and God was glorified through His Son, who had restored hope to the hopeless and strength to the stricken one. This man and his family were ready to lay down their lives for Jesus. No doubt dimmed their faith, no unbelief marred their fealty to Him who had brought light into their darkened home.

At the Pool of Bethesda

"Now there is at Jerusalem by the sheep market a pool, which is called in the Hebrew tongue Bethesda, having five porches. In these lay a great multitude of impotent folk, of blind, halt, withered, waiting for the moving of the water." John 5:2, 3.

At certain seasons the waters of this pool were agitated, and it was commonly believed that this was the result of supernatural power, and that whoever first after the troubling of the pool stepped into the waters, would be healed of whatever disease he might have. Hundreds of sufferers visited the place; but so great was the crowd when the water was troubled that they rushed forward, trampling underfoot men, women, and children weaker than themselves. Many could not get near the pool. Many who had succeeded in reaching it died upon its brink. Shelters had been erected about the place, that the sick might be protected from the heat by the day and the chilliness of the night. There were some who spent the night in these porches, creeping to the edge of the pool day after day, in the vain hope of relief.

Jesus was at Jerusalem. Walking alone, in apparent meditation and prayer, He came to the pool. He saw the wretched sufferers watching for that which they supposed to be their only chance of cure. He longed to exercise His healing power and make every sufferer whole. But it was the Sabbath day. Multitudes were going to the temple for worship, and He knew that such an act of healing would so excite the prejudice of the Jews as to cut short His work.

But the Saviour saw one case of supreme wretchedness. It was that of a man who had been a helpless cripple for

211

thirty-eight years. His disease was in a great degree the result of his own evil habits, and was looked upon as a judgment from God. Alone and friendless, feeling that he was shut out from God's mercy, the sufferer had passed long years of misery. At the time when it was expected that the water would be troubled, those who pitied his helplessness would bear him to the porches. But at the favored moment he had no one to help him in. He had seen the rippling of the water, but had never been able to get farther than the edge of the pool. Others stronger than he would plunge in before him. The poor, helpless sufferer was unable to contend successfully with the scrambling, selfish crowd. His persistent efforts toward the one object, and his anxiety and continual disappointment, were fast wearing away the remnant of his strength.

The sick man was lying on his mat, and occasionally lifting his head to gaze at the pool, when a tender, compassionate face bent over him, and the words, "Wilt thou be made whole?" arrested his attention. Hope came to his heart. He felt that in some way he was to have help. But the glow of encouragement soon faded. He remembered how often he had tried to reach the pool, and now he had little prospect of living till it should again be troubled. He turned away wearily, saying, "Sir, I have no man, when the water is troubled, to put me into the pool: but while I am coming, another steppeth down before me."

Jesus bids him, "Rise, take up thy bed, and walk." John 5:6-8. With a new hope the sick man looks upon Jesus. The expression of His countenance, the tones of His voice, are like no other. Love and power seem to breathe from His very presence. The cripple's faith takes hold upon Christ's word. Without question he sets his will to obey, and as he does this, his whole body responds.

Every nerve and muscle thrills with new life, and healthful action comes to his crippled limbs. Springing to his feet, he goes on his way with firm, free step, praising God and rejoicing in his new-found strength.

Jesus had given the palsied man no assurance of divine help. The man might have said, Lord, if Thou wilt make me whole, I will obey Thy word. He might have stopped to doubt, and thus have lost his one chance of healing. But no, he believed Christ's word, believed that he was made whole; immediately he made the effort, and God gave him the power; he willed to walk, and he did walk. Acting on the word of Christ, he was made whole.

Believe the Saviour's Word

By sin we have been severed from the life of God. Our souls are palsied. Of ourselves we are no more capable of living a holy life than was the impotent man capable of walking. Many realize their helplessness; they are longing for that spiritual life which will bring them into harmony with God, and are striving to obtain it. But in vain. In despair they cry, "O wretched man that I am! who shall deliver me from this body of death?" Romans 7:24, margin. Let these desponding, struggling ones look up. The Saviour is bending over the purchase of His blood, saying with inexpressible tenderness and pity, "Wilt thou be made whole?" He bids you arise in health and peace. Do not wait to feel that you are made whole. Believe the Saviour's word. Put your will on the side of Christ. Will to serve Him, and in acting upon His word you will receive strength. Whatever may be the evil practice, the master passion which through long indulgence binds both soul and body, Christ is able and longs to deliver. He will impart life to the soul that is "dead in trespasses." Ephesians 2:1. He will set free the captive that is held by weakness and misfortune and the chains of sin.

The Woman Taken in Sin

The Feast of Tabernacles had just ended. The priests and rabbis at Jerusalem had been defeated in their plottings against Jesus, and, as evening fell, "every man went unto his own house. Jesus went unto the Mount of Olives." John 7:53; 8:1.

From the excitement and confusion of the city, from the eager crowds and the treacherous rabbis, Jesus turned away to the quiet of the olive groves, where He could be alone with God. But in the early morning He returned to the temple; and as the people gathered about Him, He sat down and taught them.

He was soon interrupted. A group of Pharisees and scribes approached Him, dragging with them a terror-stricken woman, whom with hard, eager voices they accused of having violated the seventh commandment. Pushing her into the presence of Jesus, they said, with a hypocritical display of respect, "Master, this woman was taken in adultery, in the very act. Now Moses in the law commanded us, that such should be stoned: but what sayest Thou?" John 8:4, 5.

Their pretended reverence veiled a deep-laid plot for His ruin. Should Jesus acquit the woman, He might be charged with despising the law of Moses. Should He declare her worthy of death, He could be accused to the Romans as one who assumed authority belonging only to them.

Jesus looked upon the scene—the trembling victim in her shame, the hard-faced dignitaries, devoid of even human pity. His spirit of stainless purity shrank from the spectacle. Giving no sign that He had heard the question, He stooped, and fixing His eyes upon the ground, began to write in the dust.

Impatient at His delay and apparent indifference, the accusers drew nearer, urging the matter upon His attention. But as their eyes, following those of Jesus, fell upon the pavement at His feet, their voices were silenced. There, traced before them, were the guilty secrets of their own lives.

Rising, and fixing His eyes upon the plotting elders, Jesus said, "He that is without sin among *you,* let him first cast a stone at her." Verse 7. And stooping down, He continued writing.

He had not set aside the Mosaic law, nor infringed upon the authority of Rome. The accusers were defeated. Now, their robes of pretended holiness torn from them, they stood, guilty and condemned, in the presence of Infinite Purity. Trembling lest the hidden iniquity of their lives should be laid open to the multitude, with bowed heads and downcast eyes they stole away, leaving their victim with the pitying Saviour.

Jesus arose, and looking upon the woman, said, "Where are those thine accusers? hath no man condemned thee? She said, No man, Lord. And Jesus said unto her, Neither do I condemn thee: go, and sin no more." Verses 10, 11.

The woman had stood before Jesus, cowering with fear. His words, "He that is without sin among you, let him first cast a stone," had come to her as a death sentence. She dared not lift her eyes to the Saviour's face, but silently awaited

215

her doom. In astonishment she saw her accusers depart speechless and confounded; then those words of hope fell upon her ear, "Neither do I condemn thee: go, and sin no more." Her heart was melted, and casting herself at the feet of Jesus, she sobbed out her grateful love, and with bitter tears confessed her sins.

Beginning of a New Life

This was to her the beginning of a new life, a life of purity and peace, devoted to God. In the uplifting of this fallen soul, Jesus performed a greater miracle than in healing the most grievous physical disease; He cured the spiritual malady which is unto death everlasting. This penitent woman became one of His most steadfast followers. With self-sacrificing love and devotion she showed her gratitude for His forgiving mercy. For this erring woman the world had only contempt and scorn; but the Sinless One pitied her weakness, and reached to her a helping hand. While the hypocritical Pharisees denounced, Jesus bade her, "Go, and sin no more."

Jesus knows the circumstances of every soul. The greater the sinner's guilt, the more he needs the Saviour. His heart of divine love and sympathy is drawn out most of all for the one who is the most hopelessly entangled in the snares of the enemy. With His own blood He has signed the emancipation papers of the race.

Jesus does not desire those who have been purchased at such a cost to become the sport of the enemy's temptations. He does not desire us to be overcome, and perish. He who curbed the lions in their den, and walked with His faithful witnesses amid the fiery flames, is just as ready to work in our behalf, to subdue every evil in our nature. Today He is standing at the altar of mercy, presenting before God the prayers of those who desire His help. He turns no weeping, contrite one away. Freely will He pardon all who come to Him for forgiveness and restoration. He does not tell to any all that He might reveal, but He bids every trembling soul take courage. Whosoever will may take hold of God's strength and make peace with Him, and He will make peace.

The souls that turn to Him for refuge, Jesus lifts above the accusing and the strife of tongues. No man or evil angel can impeach these souls. Christ unites them to His own divine-human nature. They stand beside the great Sin Bearer, in the light proceeding from the throne of God.

Casting Out a Demon

In the synagogue at Capernaum, Jesus was speaking of His mission to set free the slaves of sin. He was interrupted by a shriek of terror. A madman rushed forward from among the people, crying out, "Let us alone; what have we to do with Thee, Thou Jesus of Nazareth? art Thou come to destroy us? I know Thee who Thou art, the Holy One of God."

Jesus rebuked the demon, "saying, Hold thy peace, and come out of him. And when the devil had thrown him in the midst, he came out of him, and hurt him not." Mark 1:24, 25; Luke 4:34, 35.

The cause of this man's affliction also was in his own life. He had been fascinated with the pleasures of sin, and had thought to make life a grand carnival. Intemperance and frivolity perverted the noble attributes of his nature, and Satan took entire control of him. Remorse came too late. When he would have sacrificed wealth and pleasure to re-

217

gain his lost manhood, he had become helpless in the grasp of the evil one.

In the Saviour's presence he was roused to long for freedom; but the demon resisted the power of Christ. When the man tried to appeal to Jesus for help, the evil spirit put words into his mouth, and he cried out in an agony of fear. The demoniac partially comprehended that he was in the presence of One who could set him free; but when he tried to come within reach of that mighty hand, another's will held him; another's words found utterance through him.

The conflict between the power of Satan and his own desire for freedom was terrible. It seemed that the tortured man must lose his life in the struggle with the foe that had been the ruin of his manhood. But the Saviour spoke with authority and set the captive free. The man who had been possessed stood before the wondering people in the freedom of self-possession.

With glad voice he praised God for deliverance. The eye that had so lately glared with the fire of insanity now beamed with intelligence and overflowed with grateful tears. The people were dumb with amazement. As soon as they recovered speech, they exclaimed one to another, "What is this? a new teaching! with authority He commandeth even the unclean spirits, and they obey Him." Mark 1:27, R.V.

Power Over Demons Today

There are multitudes today as truly under the power of evil spirits as was the demoniac of Capernaum. All who willfully depart from God's commandments are placing themselves under the control of Satan. Many a man tampers with evil, thinking that he can break away at pleasure; but he is lured on and on, until he finds himself controlled by a will stronger than his own. He cannot escape its mysterious power. Secret sin or master passion may hold him a captive as helpless as was the demoniac of Capernaum.

Yet his condition is not hopeless. God does not control our minds without our consent; but every man is free to choose what power he will have to rule over him. None have fallen so low, none are so vile, but that they may find deliverance in Christ. The demoniac, in place of prayer, could utter only the words of Satan; yet the heart's unspoken appeal was heard. No cry from a soul in need, though it fail of utterance in words, will be unheeded. Those who consent to enter into covenant with God are not left to the power of Satan or to the infirmity of their own nature.

Henceforth Christ's followers are to look upon Satan as a conquered foe. Upon the cross, Jesus was to gain the victory for them; that victory He desired them to accept as their own.

The rainbow of promise encircling the throne on high is an everlasting testimony that "God so loved the world, that He gave His only-begotten Son, that whosoever believeth in Him should not perish, but have everlasting life." John 3:16. It testifies to the universe that God will never forsake His children in the struggle with evil. It is an assurance to us of strength and protection as long as the throne itself shall endure.

Call to Service

IT IS morning on the Sea of Galilee. Jesus and His disciples have come to shore after a tempestuous night on the water, and the light of the rising sun touches sea and land as with the benediction of peace. But as they step upon the beach, they are greeted with a sight more terrible than the storm-tossed sea. From some hiding place among the tombs, two madmen rush upon them, as if to tear them in pieces. Hanging about these men are parts of chains which they have broken in escaping from confinement. Their flesh is torn and bleeding, their eyes glare out from their long and matted hair, the very likeness of humanity seems to have been blotted out. They look more like wild beasts than like men.

The disciples and their companions flee in terror; but presently they notice that Jesus is not with them, and they turn to look for Him. He is standing where they left Him. He who stilled the tempest, who has before met Satan and conquered him, does not flee before these demons. When the men, gnashing their teeth and foaming at the mouth, approach Him, Jesus raises that hand which has beckoned the waves to rest, and the men can come no nearer. They stand before Him, raging but helpless.

With authority He bids the unclean spirits come out of

them. The unfortunate men realize that One is near who can save them from the tormenting demons. They fall at the Saviour's feet to entreat His mercy; but when their lips are opened, the demons speak through them, crying, "What have we to do with Thee, Jesus, Thou Son of God? art Thou come hither to torment us?" Matthew 8:29.

The evil spirits are forced to release their victims, and a wonderful change comes over the demoniacs. Light shines into their minds. Their eyes beam with intelligence. The countenances so long deformed into the image of Satan become suddenly mild, the blood-stained hands are quiet, and the men lift their voices in praise to God. They desire the companionship of their Deliverer. In His presence they feel secure from the demons that have tormented their lives and wasted their manhood. As Jesus is about to enter the boat, they keep close to His side, kneel at His feet, and beg to remain near Him, where they may listen to His words. But Jesus bids them go home and tell what great things the Lord has done for them.

Here is a work for them to do—to go to a heathen home and tell of the blessings they have received from Jesus. It is hard for them to be separated from the Saviour. Great difficulties will beset them in association with their heathen countrymen. And their long isolation from society seems to have disqualified them for this work. But as soon as He points out their duty, they are ready to obey.

Not only did they tell their own households and neighbors about Jesus, but they went throughout Decapolis, everywhere declaring His power to save, and describing how He had freed them from the demons.

Though the people of Gergesa had not received Jesus,

221

He did not leave them to the darkness they had chosen. When they bade Him depart from them, they had not heard His words. They were ignorant of that which they were rejecting. Therefore He sent the light to them, and by those to whom they would not refuse to listen.

First Missionaries to Decapolis

The two restored demoniacs were the first missionaries whom Christ sent to teach the gospel in the region of Decapolis. For a short time only, these men had listened to His words. Not one sermon from His lips had ever fallen upon their ears. They could not instruct the people as the disciples who had been daily with Christ were able to do. But they could tell what they knew; what they themselves had seen, and heard, and felt of the Saviour's power. This is what everyone can do whose heart has been touched by the grace of God. This is the witness for which our Lord calls, and for want of which the world is perishing.

The gospel is to be presented, not as a lifeless theory, but as a living force to change the life. God would have His servants bear testimony to the fact that through His grace men may possess Christlikeness of character, and may rejoice in the assurance of His great love. He would have us bear testimony to the fact that He cannot be satisfied until all who will accept salvation are reclaimed and reinstated in their holy privileges as His sons and daughters.

Even those whose course has been most offensive to Him He freely accepts. When they repent, He imparts to them His divine Spirit, and sends them forth into the camp of the disloyal to proclaim His mercy. Souls that have been degraded into instruments of Satan are still, through the power of Christ, transformed into messengers of righteousness, and are sent forth to tell how great things the Lord hath done for them, and hath had compassion on them.

After the woman of Capernaum had been healed by the touch of faith, Jesus desired her to acknowledge the blessing she had received. The gifts which the gospel offers are not to be secured by stealth or enjoyed in secret.

> "Ye are My witnesses, saith the Lord,
>   That I am God." Isaiah 43:12.

Our confession of His faithfulness is Heaven's chosen agency for revealing Christ to the world. We are to acknowledge His grace as made known through the holy men of old; but that which will be most effectual is the testimony of our own experience. We are witnesses for God as we reveal in ourselves the working of a power that is divine. Every individual has a life distinct from all others, and an experience differing essentially from theirs. God desires that our praise shall ascend to Him, marked with our own individuality. These precious acknowledgments to the praise of the glory of His grace, when supported by a Christlike life, have an irresistible power that works for the salvation of souls.

A True Light Bearer

The Samaritan woman who talked with Jesus at Jacob's well had no sooner found the Saviour than she brought others to Him. She proved herself a more effective missionary than His own disciples. The disciples saw nothing in Samaria to indicate that it was an encouraging field. Their thoughts were fixed upon a great work to be done in the future. They did not see that right around them was a

223

harvest to be gathered. But through the woman whom they despised, a whole cityful were brought to hear Jesus. She carried the light at once to her countrymen.

This woman represents the working of a practical faith in Christ. Every true disciple is born into the kingdom of God as a missionary. No sooner does he come to know the Saviour than he desires to make others acquainted with Him. The saving and sanctifying truth cannot be shut up in his heart. He who drinks of the living water becomes a fountain of life. The receiver becomes a giver. The grace of Christ in the soul is like a spring in the desert, welling up to refresh all, and making those who are ready to perish eager to drink of the water of life. In doing this work a greater blessing is received than if we work merely to benefit ourselves. It is in working to spread the good news of salvation that we are brought near to the Saviour.

Of those who receive His grace the Lord says: "I will make them and the places round about My hill a blessing; and I will cause the shower to come down in its season; there shall be showers of blessing." Ezekiel 34:26, R.V.

The Example of Jesus

For three years the disciples had before them the wonderful example of Jesus. Day by day they walked and talked with Him, hearing His words of cheer to the weary and heavy-laden, and seeing the manifestations of His power in behalf of the sick and afflicted. When the time came for Him to leave them, He gave them grace and power to carry forward His work in His name. They were to shed abroad the light of His gospel of love and healing. And the Saviour promised that His presence would be always with them.

Through the Holy Spirit He would be even nearer to them than when He walked visibly among men.

The work which the disciples did, we also are to do. Every Christian is to be a missionary. In sympathy and compassion we are to minister to those in need of help, seeking with unselfish earnestness to lighten the woes of suffering humanity.

All may find something to do. None need feel that there is no place where they can labor for Christ. The Saviour identifies Himself with every child of humanity. That we might become members of the heavenly family, He became a member of the earthly family. He is the Son of man, and thus a brother to every son and daughter of Adam. His followers are not to feel themselves detached from the perishing world around them. They are a part of the great web of humanity, and heaven looks upon them as brothers to sinners as well as to saints.

Millions upon millions of human beings, in sickness and ignorance and sin, have never so much as heard of Christ's love for them. Were our condition and theirs to be reversed, what would we desire them to do for us? All this, so far as lies in our power, we are to do for them. Christ's rule of life by which every one of us must stand or fall in the judgment is, "Whatsoever ye would that men should do to you, do ye even so to them." Matthew 7:12.

By all that has given us advantage over another—be it education and refinement, nobility of character, Christian training, religious experience—we are in debt to those less favored; and, so far as lies in our power, we are to minister unto them. If we are strong, we are to stay up the hands of the weak.

Angels of glory that do always behold the face of the Father in heaven, joy in ministering to His little ones. Angels are ever present where they are most needed, with those who have the hardest battles with self to fight, and whose surroundings are the most discouraging. Weak and trembling souls who have many objectionable traits of character are their special charge. That which selfish hearts would regard as humiliating service, ministering to those who are wretched and in every way inferior in character, is the work of the pure, sinless beings from the courts above.

Jesus did not consider heaven a place to be desired while we were lost. He left the heavenly courts for a life of reproach and insult, and a death of shame. He who was rich in heaven's priceless treasure became poor, that through His poverty we might be rich. We are to follow in the path He trod.

He who becomes a child of God should henceforth look upon himself as a link in the chain let down to save the world, one with Christ in His plan of mercy, going forth with Him to seek and save the lost.

Today no curious multitudes flock to the desert places to see and hear the Christ. His voice is not heard in the busy streets. No cry sounds from the wayside, "Jesus of Nazareth passeth by." Luke 18:37.

Yet this word is true today. Christ walks unseen through our streets. With messages of mercy He comes to our homes. With all who are seeking to minister in His name, He waits to cooperate. He is in the midst of us, to heal and to bless, if we will receive Him.

May We Know God?

LIKE our Saviour, we are in this world to do service for God. We are here to become like God in character, and by a life of service to reveal Him to the world. In order to be co-workers with God, in order to become like Him and to reveal His character, we must know Him aright. We must know Him as He reveals Himself.

A knowledge of God is the foundation of all true education and of all true service. It is the only real safeguard against temptation. It is this alone that can make us like God in character.

This is the knowledge needed by all who are working for the uplifting of their fellowmen. Transformation of character, purity of life, efficiency in service, adherence to correct principles, all depend upon a right knowledge of God. This knowledge is the essential preparation both for this life and for the life to come.

"The knowledge of the Holy is understanding." Proverbs 9:10.

Through a knowledge of Him are "given unto us all things that pertain unto life and godliness." 2 Peter 1:3.

"This is life eternal," said Jesus, "that they might know Thee the only true God, and Jesus Christ, whom Thou hast sent." John 17:3. See also Jeremiah 9:23, 24.

We need to study the revelations of Himself that God has given.

"Acquaint now thyself with Him,
   And be at peace:
   Thereby good shall come unto thee." Job 22:21, A.R.V.

"The invisible things of Him since the creation of the world are clearly seen, being perceived through the things that are made, even His everlasting power and divinity." Romans 1:20, R.V.

The things of nature that we now behold give us but a faint conception of Eden's glory. Sin has marred earth's beauty; on all things may be seen traces of the work of evil. Yet much that is beautiful remains. Nature testifies that One infinite in power, great in goodness, mercy, and love, created the earth, and filled it with life and gladness. Even in their blighted state, all things reveal the handiwork of the great Master Artist. Wherever we turn we may hear the voice of God and see evidences of His goodness.

From the solemn roll of the deep-toned thunder and old ocean's ceaseless roar, to the glad songs that make the forests vocal with melody, nature's ten thousand voices speak His praise. In earth and sea and sky with their marvelous tint and color, varying in gorgeous contrast or blended in harmony, we behold His glory. The everlasting hills tell us of His power. The trees that wave their green banners in the sunlight, and the flowers in their delicate beauty, point to their Creator. The living green that carpets the brown earth tells of God's care for the humblest of His creatures. The caves of the sea and the depths of the earth reveal His treasures. He who placed the pearls in the ocean and the amethyst and chrysolite among the rocks, is a lover of the beautiful. The sun rising in the heavens is a representative of Him who is the life and light of all that He has made. All the brightness and beauty that adorn the earth and light up the heavens speak of God.

"His glory covered the heavens." Habakkuk 3:3.
"The earth is full of Thy riches." Psalm 104:24.

"Day unto day uttereth speech,
And night unto night showeth knowledge.
There is no speech nor language,
Without these their voice is heard.
Their line is gone out through all the earth,
And their words to the end of the world."
Psalm 19:2-4, margin.

All things tell of His tender, fatherly care, and of His desire to make His children happy.

The mighty power that works through all nature and sustains all things is not, as some men of science represent, merely an all-pervading principle, an actuating energy. God is a Spirit; yet He is a personal being; for so He has revealed Himself:

"The Lord is the true God,
He is the living God, and an everlasting King. . . .
The gods that have not made the heavens and the earth,
Even they shall perish from the earth, and from under
these heavens."
"The portion of Jacob is not like them:
For He is the former of all things."
"He hath made the earth by His power,
He hath established the world by His wisdom,
And hath stretched out the heavens by His discretion."
Jeremiah 10:10, 11, 16, 12.

229

God's handiwork in nature is not God Himself in nature. The things of nature are an expression of God's character and power; but we are not to regard nature as God. The artistic skill of human beings produces very beautiful workmanship, things that delight the eye, and these things reveal to us something of the thought of the designer; but the thing made is not the maker. It is not the work, but the workman, that is counted worthy of honor. So, while nature is an expression of God's thought, it is not nature, but the God of nature, that is to be exalted.

"He that buildeth His spheres in the heaven,
And hath founded His arch in the earth;"
"He that calleth for the waters of the sea,
And poureth them out upon the face of the earth;
Jehovah is His Name."

Amos 9:6, K.J.V., margin; Noyes's
translation; A.R.V.

The work of creation cannot be explained by science. What science can explain the mystery of life?

"Through faith we understand that the worlds were framed by the word of God, so that things which are seen were not made of things which do appear." Hebrews 11:3.

"I form the light, and create darkness: . . .
I the Lord do all these things."
"I have made the earth,
And created man upon it:
I, even My hands, have stretched out the heavens,
And all their host have I commanded."
"When I call unto them, they stand up together."

Isaiah 45:7, 12; 48:13.

In the creation of the earth, God was not indebted to pre-existing matter. "He spake, and it was done; He commanded, and it stood fast." Psalm 33:9. All things, material or spiritual, stood up before the Lord Jehovah at His voice, and were created for His own purpose. The heavens and all the host of them, the earth and all things therein, came into existence by the breath of His mouth.

Man Created in God's Image

In the creation of man was manifest the agency of a personal God. When God had made man in His image, the human form was perfect in all its arrangements, but it was without life. Then a personal, self-existing God breathed in that form the breath of life, and man became a living, intelligent being. All parts of the human organism were set in action. The heart, the arteries, the veins, the tongue, the hands, the feet, the senses, the faculties of the mind— all began their work, and all were placed under law. Man became a living soul. Through Christ, the Word, a personal God created man, and endowed him with intelligence and power.

Our substance was not hid from Him when we were made in secret; His eyes saw our substance, yet being imperfect, and in His book all our members were written, when as yet there were none of them.

Above all lower orders of being, God designed that man, the crowning work of His creation, should express His thought and reveal His glory. But man is not to exalt himself as God.

God is constantly employed in upholding and using as His servants the things that He has made. He works through

231

the laws of nature, using them as His instruments. They are not self-acting. Nature in her work testifies of the intelligent presence and active agency of a Being who moves in all things according to His will.

"Whatsoever the Lord pleased, that did He
In heaven, and in earth, in the seas, and all deep places."
"He commanded, and they were created.
He hath also stablished them forever and ever:
He hath made a decree which shall not pass."
Psalms 135:6; 148:5, 6.

It is not by inherent power that year by year the earth yields its bounties and continues its march around the sun. The hand of the Infinite One is perpetually at work guiding this planet. It is God's power continually exercised that keeps the earth in position in its rotation. It is God who causes the sun to rise in the heavens. He opens the windows of heaven and gives rain.

"He giveth snow like wool:
He scattereth the hoarfrost like ashes."
Psalm 147:16.

"When He uttereth His voice, there is a multitude of
waters in the heavens,
And He causeth the vapors to ascend from the ends of
the earth;
He maketh lightnings with rain,
And bringeth forth the wind out of His treasures."
Jeremiah 10:13.

It is by His power that vegetation is caused to flourish, that every leaf appears, every flower blooms, every fruit develops.

In Him We Live and Move

The mechanism of the human body cannot be fully understood; it presents mysteries that baffle the most intelligent. It is not as the result of a mechanism, which, once set in motion, continues its work, that the pulse beats, and breath follows breath. In God we live and move and have our being. The beating heart, the throbbing pulse, every nerve and muscle in the living organism, is kept in order and activity by the power of an ever-present God.

The Bible shows us God in His high and holy place, not in a state of inactivity, not in silence and solitude, but surrounded by ten thousand times ten thousand and thousands of thousands of holy beings, all waiting to do His will. Through these messengers He is in active communication with every part of His dominion. By His Spirit He is everywhere present. Through the agency of His Spirit and His angels He ministers to the children of men.

Above the distractions of the earth He sits enthroned; all things are open to His divine survey; and from His great and calm eternity He orders that which His providence sees best.

> "The way of man is not in himself:
> It is not in man that walketh to direct his steps."
> Jeremiah 10:23.
> "The eye of the Lord is upon them that fear Him,
> Upon them that hope in His mercy;
> To deliver their soul from death,
> And to keep them alive in famine."
> "How precious is Thy loving-kindness, O God!
> And the children of men take refuge under the shadow
> of Thy wings."

"Happy is he that hath the God of Jacob for his help,
Whose hope is in the Lord his God."

Psalms 33:18, 19; 36:7, R.V.; 146:5.

"The earth, O Jehovah, is full of Thy loving-kindness."
Thou lovest "righteousness and justice."
Thou "art the confidence of all the ends of the earth,
And of them that are afar off upon the sea:
Who by His strength setteth fast the mountains,
Being girded about with might;
Who stilleth the roaring of the seas, . . .
And the tumult of the peoples."

Psalms 119:64; 33:5; 65:5-7, A.R.V.

"The Lord upholdeth all that fall,
And raiseth up all those that be bowed down.
The eyes of all wait upon Thee;
And Thou givest them their meat in due season.
Thou openest Thine hand,
And satisfiest the desire of every living thing."

Psalm 145:14-16.

God a Personal Being

As a personal being, God has revealed Himself in His Son. The outshining of the Father's glory, "and the express image of His person" (Hebrews 1:3), Jesus, as a personal Saviour, came to the world. As a personal Saviour, He ascended on high. As a personal Saviour, He intercedes in the heavenly courts. Before the throne of God in our behalf ministers "One like unto the Son of man." Revelaton 1:13.

Christ, the Light of the world, veiled the dazzling splendor of His divinity, and came to live as a man among men that they might, without being consumed, become acquainted with their Creator. Since sin brought separation between

234

man and his Maker, no man has seen God at any time, except as He is manifested through Christ.

"I and My Father are one," Christ declared. John 10:30. "No man knoweth the Son, but the Father; neither knoweth any man the Father, save the Son, and he to whomsoever the Son will reveal Him." Matthew 11:27.

Christ came to teach human beings what God desires them to know. In the heavens above, in the earth, in the broad waters of the ocean, we see the handiwork of God. All created things testify to His power, His wisdom, His love. Yet not from the stars or the ocean or the cataract can we learn of the personality of God as it was revealed in Christ.

God saw that a clearer revelation than nature was needed to portray both His personality and His character. He sent His Son into the world to manifest, so far as could be endured by human sight, the nature and the attributes of the invisible God.

Let us study the words that Christ spoke in the upper chamber, on the night before His crucifixion. He was nearing His hour of trial, and He sought to comfort His disciples, who were to be so severely tempted and tried.

"Let not your heart be troubled," He said. "Ye believe in God, believe also in Me. In My Father's house are many mansions: if it were not so, I would have told you. I go to prepare a place for you. . . .

"Thomas saith unto Him, Lord, we know not whither Thou goest; and how can we know the way? Jesus saith unto him, I am the way, the truth, and the life: no man cometh unto the Father, but by Me. If ye had known Me, ye should have known My Father also: and from henceforth ye know Him, and have seen Him.

"Philip saith unto Him, Lord, show us the Father, and it sufficeth us. Jesus saith unto him, Have I been so long time with you, and yet hast thou not known Me, Philip? he that hath seen Me hath seen the Father; and how sayest thou then, Show us the Father? Believest thou not that I am in the Father, and the Father in Me? the words that I speak unto you I speak not of Myself: but the Father that dwelleth in Me, He doeth the works." John 14:1-10.

The disciples did not yet understand Christ's words concerning His relation to God. Much of His teaching was still dark to them. Christ desired them to have a clearer, more distinct knowledge of God.

"These things have I spoken unto you in parables," He said; "but the time cometh, when I shall no more speak unto you in parables, but I shall show you plainly of the Father." John 16:25, margin.

Limitations of Our Knowledge

When, on the Day of Pentecost, the Holy Spirit was poured out on the disciples, they understood more fully the truths that Christ had spoken in parables. Much of the teaching that had been a mystery to them was made clear. But not even then did the disciples receive the complete fulfillment of Christ's promise. They received all the knowledge of God that they could bear, but the complete fulfillment of the promise that Christ would show them plainly of the Father was yet to come. Thus it is today. Our knowledge of God is partial and imperfect. When the conflict is ended, and the Man Christ Jesus acknowledges before the Father His faithful workers who in a world of sin have borne true witness for Him, they will understand clearly what now are mysteries to them.

Christ took with Him to the heavenly courts His glorified humanity. To those who receive Him He gives power to become the sons of God, that at last God may receive them as His, to dwell with Him throughout eternity. If during this life they are loyal to God, they will at last "see His face; and His name shall be in their foreheads." Revelation 22:4. And what is the happiness of heaven but to see God? What greater joy could come to the sinner saved by the grace of Christ than to look upon the face of God and know Him as Father?

The Scriptures clearly indicate the relation between God and Christ, and they bring to view as clearly the personality and individuality of each.

"God, who at sundry times and in divers manners spake in time past unto the fathers by the prophets, hath in these last days spoken unto us by His Son; . . . who being the brightness of His glory, and the express image of His person, and upholding all things by the word of His power, when He had by Himself purged our sins, sat down on the right hand of the Majesty on high; being made so much better than the angels, as He hath by inheritance obtained a more excellent name than they. For unto which of the angels said He at any time, Thou art My Son, this day have I begotten thee? And again, I will be to Him a Father, and He shall be to Me a Son?" Hebrews 1:1-5.

The personality of the Father and the Son, also the unity that exists between them, are presented in the seventeenth chapter of John, in the prayer of Christ for His disciples:

"Neither pray I for these alone, but for them also which shall believe on Me through their word; that they all may be one; as Thou, Father, art in Me, and I in Thee, that

237

they also may be one in Us: that the world may believe that Thou hast sent Me." John 17:20, 21.

The unity that exists between Christ and His disciples does not destroy the personality of either. They are one in purpose, in mind, in character, but not in person. It is thus that God and Christ are one.

Taking humanity upon Him, Christ came to be one with humanity, and at the same time to reveal our heavenly Father to sinful human beings. He who had been in the presence of the Father from the beginning, He who was the express image of the invisible God, was alone able to reveal the character of the Deity to mankind. He was in all things made like unto His brethren. He became flesh, even as we are. He was hungry and thirsty and weary. He was sustained by food and refreshed by sleep. He shared the lot of men; yet He was the blameless Son of God. He was a stranger and sojourner on the earth—in the world, but not of the world; tempted and tried as men and women today are tempted and tried, yet living a life free from sin. Tender, compassionate, sympathetic, ever considerate of others, He represented the character of God, and was constantly engaged in service for God and man.

"Jehovah hath anointed Me," He said,
"To preach good tidings unto the poor;
 He hath sent Me to bind up the brokenhearted,
 To proclaim liberty to the captives,"
"And recovering of sight to the blind,"
"To proclaim the year of Jehovah's favor; . . .
 To comfort all that mourn."

Isaiah 61:1, A.R.V., margin;
Luke 4:18; Isaiah 61:2, A.R.V.

"Love your enemies," He bids us; "bless them that curse you, do good to them that hate you, and pray for them which despitefully use you, and persecute you; that ye may be the children of your Father which is in heaven:" "for He is kind unto the unthankful and to the evil." Matthew 5:44, 45; Luke 6:35. "He maketh His sun to rise on the evil and on the good, and sendeth rain on the just and on the unjust." Matthew 5:45. "Be ye therefore merciful, as your Father also is merciful." Luke 6:36.

Love Centers in the Cross

The revelation of God's love to man centers in the cross. Its full significance tongue cannot utter, pen cannot portray, the mind of man cannot comprehend. Looking upon the cross of Calvary we can only say, "God so loved the world, that He gave His only-begotten Son, that whosoever believeth in Him should not perish, but have everlasting life." John 3:16.

Christ crucified for our sins, Christ risen from the dead, Christ ascended on high, is the science of salvation that we are to learn and to teach.

It is through the gift of Christ that we receive every blessing. Through that gift there comes to us day by day the unfailing flow of Jehovah's goodness. Every flower, with its delicate tints and its fragrance, is given for our enjoyment through that one gift. The sun and the moon were made by Him. There is not a star which beautifies the heavens that He did not make. Every drop of rain that falls, every ray of light shed upon our unthankful world, testifies to the love of God in Christ. Everything is supplied to us through the one unspeakable Gift, God's only-begotten Son. He was nailed to the cross that all these bounties might flow to God's workmanship.

"Behold, what manner of love the Father hath bestowed upon us, that we should be called the sons of God." 1 John 3:1.

"Men have not heard, nor perceived by the ear,
Neither hath the eye seen a God besides Thee,
Who worketh for him that waiteth for Him."
Isaiah 64:4, A.R.V.

The knowledge of God as revealed in Christ is the knowledge that all who are saved must have. It is the knowledge that works transformation of character. This knowledge, received, will re-create the soul in the image of God. It will impart to the whole being a spiritual power that is divine.

This is the knowledge which God is inviting us to receive, and beside which all else is vanity and nothingness.

The Quest for Truth

MORE clearly than we do we need to understand the issues at stake in the great conflict in which we are engaged. We need to understand more fully the value of the truths of the Word of God, and the danger of allowing our minds to be diverted from them by the great deceiver.

The infinite value of the sacrifice required for our redemption reveals the fact that sin is a tremendous evil. Through sin the whole human organism is deranged, the mind is perverted, the imagination corrupted. Sin has degraded the faculties of the soul. Temptations from without find an answering chord within the heart, and the feet turn imperceptibly toward evil.

As the sacrifice in our behalf was complete, so our restoration from the defilement of sin is to be complete. No act of wickedness will the law of God excuse; no unrighteousness can escape its condemnation. The ethics of the gospel acknowledge no standard but the perfection of the divine character. The life of Christ was a perfect fulfillment of every precept of the law. He said, "I have kept My Father's commandments." John 15:10. His life is our example of obedience and service. God alone can renew the heart. "It is God which worketh in you both to will and to do of His good pleasure." But we are bidden, "Work out your own salvation." Philippians 2:13, 12.

Wrongs cannot be righted, nor can reformations in conduct be made, by a few feeble, intermittent efforts. Character building is the work, not of a day, nor of a year, but of a lifetime. The struggle for conquest over self, for holiness and heaven, is a lifelong struggle. Without continual effort and constant activity, there can be no advancement in the divine life, no attainment of the victor's crown.

The strongest evidence of man's fall from a higher state is the fact that it costs so much to return. The way of return can be gained only by hard fighting, inch by inch, hour by hour. In one moment, by a hasty, unguarded act, we may place ourselves in the power of evil; but it requires more than a moment to break the fetters and attain to a holier life. The purpose may be formed, the work begun; but its accomplishment will require toil, time, perseverance, patience, and sacrifice.

We cannot allow ourselves to act from impulse. We cannot be off guard for a moment. Beset with temptations without number, we must resist firmly or be conquered. Should we come to the close of life with our work undone, it would be an eternal loss.

The life of the apostle Paul was a constant conflict with self. He said, "I die daily." 1 Corinthians 15:31. His will and his desires every day conflicted with duty and the will of God. Instead of following inclination, he did God's will, however crucifying to his nature.

At the close of his life of conflict, looking back over its struggles and triumphs, he could say, "I have fought a good fight, I have finished my course, I have kept the faith: henceforth there is laid up for me a crown of righteousness, which the Lord, the righteous Judge, shall give me at that day." 2 Timothy 4:7, 8.

The Christian life is a battle and a march. In this warfare there is no release; the effort must be continuous and persevering. It is by unceasing endeavor that we maintain the victory over the temptations of Satan. Christian integrity must be sought with resistless energy, and maintained with a resolute fixedness of purpose.

No one will be borne upward without stern, persevering effort in his own behalf. All must engage in this warfare for themselves; no one else can fight our battles. Individually we are responsible for the issues of the struggle; though Noah, Job, and Daniel were in the land they could deliver neither son nor daughter by their righteousness.

A Science to Be Mastered

There is a science of Christianity to be mastered—a science as much deeper, broader, higher than any human science as the heavens are higher than the earth. The mind is to be disciplined, educated, trained; for we are to do service for God in ways that are not in harmony with inborn inclination. Hereditary and cultivated tendencies to evil must be overcome. Often the education and training of a lifetime must be discarded, that one may become a learner in the school of Christ. Our hearts must be educated to become steadfast in God. We are to form habits of thought that will enable us to resist temptation. We must learn to look upward. The principles of the Word of God—principles that are as high as heaven, and that compass eternity—we are to understand in their bearing upon our daily life.

Every act, every word, every thought, is to be in accord with these principles. All must be brought into harmony with, and subject to, Christ.

The precious graces of the Holy Spirit are not developed in a moment. Courage, fortitude, meekness, faith, unwavering trust in God's power to save, are acquired by the experience of years. By a life of holy endeavor and firm adherence to the right, the children of God are to seal their destiny.

We have no time to lose. We know not how soon our probation may close. At the longest, we have but a brief lifetime here, and we know not how soon the arrow of death may strike our hearts. We know not how soon we may be called to give up the world and all its interests. Eternity stretches before us. The curtain is about to be lifted. But a few short years, and for everyone now numbered with the living the mandate will go forth:

"He that is unjust, let him be unjust still: . . . and he that is righteous, let him be righteous still: and he that is holy, let him be holy still." Revelation 22:11.

Are we prepared? Have we become acquainted with God, the Governor of heaven, the Lawgiver, and with Jesus Christ whom He sent into the world as His representative? When our lifework is ended, shall we be able to say, as did Christ our Example: "I have glorified Thee on the earth: I have finished the work which Thou gavest Me to do. . . . I have manifested Thy name"? John 17:4-6.

The angels of God are seeking to attract us from ourselves and from earthly things. Let them not labor in vain.

Minds that have been given up to loose thought need to change. "Gird up the loins of your mind, be sober, and hope to the end for the grace that is to be brought unto you at the revelation of Jesus Christ; as obedient children, not fashioning yourselves according to the former lusts in your ignorance: but as He which hath called you is holy, so be ye holy in all manner of conversation; because it is written, Be ye holy; for I am holy." 1 Peter 1:13-16.

Overcoming As Christ Overcame

The thoughts must be centered upon God. We must put forth earnest effort to overcome the evil tendencies of the natural heart. Our efforts, our self-denial and perseverance, must be proportionate to the infinite value of the object of which we are in pursuit. Only by overcoming as Christ overcame shall we win the crown of life.

Man's great danger is in being self-deceived, indulging self-sufficiency, and thus separating from God, the Source of his strength. Our natural tendencies, unless corrected by the Holy Spirit of God, have in them the seeds of moral death. Unless we become vitally connected with God, we cannot resist the unhallowed effects of self-indulgence, self-love, and temptation to sin.

In order to receive help from Christ, we must realize our need. We must have a true knowledge of ourselves. It is only he who knows himself to be a sinner that Christ can save. Only as we see our utter helplessness and renounce all self-trust, shall we lay hold on divine power.

It is not only at the beginning of the Christian life that this renunciation of self is to be made. At every advance step heavenward it is to be renewed. All our good works are dependent on a power outside of ourselves; therefore there needs to be a continual reaching out of the heart after God, a constant, earnest confession of sin and humbling

245

of the soul before Him. Perils surround us, and we are safe only as we feel our weakness and cling with the grasp of faith to our mighty Deliverer.

Turn From the Trivial

We must turn away from a thousand topics that invite attention. There are matters that consume time and arouse inquiry, but end in nothing. The highest interests demand the close attention and energy that are so often given to comparatively insignificant things.

Accepting new theories does not in itself bring new life to the soul. Even an acquaintance with facts and theories important in themselves is of little value unless put to a practical use. We need to feel our responsibility to give our souls food that will nourish and stimulate spiritual life.

The question for us to study is, "What is truth—the truth that is to be cherished, loved, honored, and obeyed?" The devotees of science have been defeated and disheartened in their efforts to find out God. What they need to inquire at this time is, "What is the truth that will enable us to win the salvation of our souls?"

"What think ye of Christ?"—this is the all-important question. Do you receive Him as a personal Saviour? To all who receive Him He gives power to become sons of God.

Christ revealed God to His disciples in a way that performed in their hearts a special work, such as He desires to do in our hearts. There are many who, in dwelling too largely upon theory, have lost sight of the living power of the Saviour's example. They have lost sight of Him as the humble, self-denying worker. What they need is to behold Jesus. Daily we need the fresh revealing of His presence.

We need to follow more closely His example of self-renunciation and self-sacrifice.

We need the experience that Paul had when he wrote: "I am crucified with Christ: nevertheless I live; yet not I, but Christ liveth in me: and the life which I now live in the flesh I live by the faith of the Son of God, who loved me, and gave Himself for me." Galatians 2:20.

The knowledge of God and of Jesus Christ expressed in character is an exaltation above everything else that is esteemed on earth or in heaven. It is the very highest education. It is the key that opens the portals of the heavenly City. This knowledge it is God's purpose that all who put on Christ shall possess.

The Incomparable Book

THE whole Bible is a revelation of the glory of God in Christ. Received, believed, obeyed, it is the great instrumentality in the transformation of character. It is the grand stimulus, the constraining force, that quickens the physical, mental, and spiritual powers, and directs the life into right channels.

The reason why the youth, and even those of mature years, are so easily led into temptation and sin is that they do not study the Word of God and meditate upon it as they should. The lack of firm, decided willpower, which is manifest in life and character, results from neglect of the sacred instruction of God's Word.

The truths of the Bible, received, will uplift mind and soul. If the Word of God were appreciated as it should be, both young and old would possess an inward rectitude, a strength of principle, that would enable them to resist temptation.

Let men teach and write the precious things of the Holy Scriptures. Let the thought, the aptitude, the keen exercise of brainpower, be given to the study of the thoughts of God. Study not the philosophy of man's conjectures, but study the philosophy of Him who is truth. No other literature can compare with this in value.

The mind that is earthly finds no pleasure in contemplating the Word of God; but for the mind renewed by the Holy Spirit, divine beauty and celestial light shine from the sacred page. That which to the earthly mind was a desolate wilderness, to the spiritual mind becomes a land of living streams.

God Revealed in His Word

The knowledge of God as revealed in His Word is the knowledge to be given to our children. From the earliest dawn of reason they should be made familiar with the name and the life of Jesus. Their first lessons should teach them that God is their Father. Their first training should be that of loving obedience. Reverently and tenderly let the Word of God be read and repeated to them, in portions suited to their comprehension and adapted to awaken their interest. And above all, let them learn of His love revealed in Christ, and its great lesson:

"If God so loved us, we ought also to love one another." 1 John 4:11.

Let the youth make the Word of God the food of mind and soul. Let the cross of Christ be made the science of all education, the center of all teaching and all study. Let it be brought into the daily experience in practical life. So will the Saviour become to the youth a daily Companion and Friend. Every thought will be brought into captivity to the obedience of Christ. With the apostle Paul they will be able to say:

"God forbid that I should glory, save in the cross of our Lord Jesus Christ, by whom the world is crucified unto me, and I unto the world." Galatians 6:14.

Thus through faith they come to know God by an experimental knowledge. They have proved for themselves the reality of His word, the truth of His promises. They have tasted, and they know that the Lord is good.

The beloved John had a knowledge gained through his own experience. He could testify:

"That which was from the beginning, which we have heard, which we have seen with our eyes, which we have looked upon, and our hands have handled, of the Word of life; (for the life was manifested, and we have seen it, and bear witness, and show unto you that eternal life, which was with the Father, and was manifested unto us;) that which we have seen and heard declare we unto you, that ye also may have fellowship with us: and truly our fellowship is with the Father, and with His Son Jesus Christ." 1 John 1:1-3.

So everyone may be able, through his own experience, to "set his seal to this, that God is true." John 3:33, R.V. He can bear witness to that which he himself has seen and heard and felt of the power of Christ. He can testify:

"I needed help, and I found it in Jesus. Every want was supplied, the hunger of my soul was satisfied; the Bible is to me the revelation of Christ. I believe in Jesus because He is to me a divine Saviour. I believe the Bible because I have found it to be the voice of God to my soul."

He who has gained a knowledge of God and His Word through personal experience is prepared to engage in the study of natural science. Of Christ it is written, "In Him was life; and the life was the light of men." John 1:4. Before the entrance of sin, Adam and Eve in Eden were surrounded with a clear and beautiful light, the light of God. This light illuminated everything which they approached. There was nothing to obscure their perception of the character or the works of God. But when they yielded to the tempter, the light departed from them. In losing the garments of holiness, they lost the light that had illuminated nature. No longer could they read it aright. They could not discern the character of God in His works. So today man cannot of himself read aright the teaching of nature. Unless guided by divine wisdom, he exalts nature and the laws of nature above nature's God. This is why mere human ideas in regard to science so often contradict the teaching of God's Word. But for those who receive the light of the life of Christ, nature is again illuminated. In the light shining from the cross, we can rightly interpret nature's teaching.

The Study of Natural Science

He who has a knowledge of God and His Word through personal experience has a settled faith in the divinity of the Holy Scriptures. He has proved that God's Word is truth, and he knows that truth can never contradict itself. He does not test the Bible by men's ideas of science; he brings these ideas to the test of the unerring standard. He knows that in true science there can be nothing contrary to the teaching of the Word; since both have the same Author, a correct understanding of both will prove them to be in harmony. Whatever in so-called scientific teaching contradicts the testimony of God's Word is mere human guesswork.

To such a student, scientific research will open vast fields of thought and information. As he contemplates the things of nature, a new perception of truth comes to him. The book of nature and the Written Word shed light upon each other. Both make him better acquainted with God by teaching him

251

of His character and of the laws through which He works.

The experience of the psalmist is the experience that all may gain by receiving God's word through nature and through revelation. He says:

"Thou, Lord, hast made me glad through Thy work:
I will triumph in the works of Thy hands."
Psalm 92:4.

"Thy mercy, O Lord, is in the heavens;
And Thy faithfulness reacheth unto the clouds.
Thy righteousness is like the great mountains;
Thy judgments are a great deep. . . .
How excellent is Thy loving-kindness, O God!"
Psalm 36:5-7.

"Blessed are they that are upright in way,
Who walk in the law of Jehovah.
Blessed are they that keep His testimonies,
That seek Him with the whole heart."
"Wherewith shall a young man cleanse his way?
By taking heed thereto according to Thy Word."
"I have chosen the way of faithfulness:
Thine ordinances have I set before me."
Psalm 119:1, 2, 9, 30, A.R.V., margin.

"Thy Word have I laid up in my heart,
That I might not sin against Thee."
Psalm 119:11, A.R.V.

Clearer Revelations of God

It is our privilege to reach higher and still higher, for clearer revealings of the character of God. When Moses prayed, "I beseech Thee, show me Thy glory," the Lord did not rebuke him, but He granted his prayer. God declared to His servant, "I will make all My goodness pass before thee, and I will proclaim the name of the Lord before thee." Exodus 33:18, 19.

It is sin that darkens our minds and dims our perceptions. As sin is purged from our hearts, the light of the knowledge of the glory of God in the face of Jesus Christ, illuminating His Word and reflected from the face of nature, more and more fully will declare Him "merciful and gracious, long-suffering, and abundant in goodness and truth." Exodus 34:6.

In His light shall we see light, until mind and heart and soul are transformed into the image of His holiness.

For those who thus lay hold of the divine assurances of God's Word, there are wonderful possibilities. Before them lie vast fields of truth, vast resources of power. Glorious things are to be revealed. Privileges and duties which they do not even suspect to be in the Bible will be made manifest. All who walk in the path of humble obedience, fulfilling His purpose, will know more and more of the oracles of God.

Let the student take the Bible as his guide, and stand firm for principle, and he may aspire to any height of attainment. All the philosophies of human nature have led to confusion and shame when God has not been recognized as all in all. But the precious faith inspired of God imparts strength and nobility of character. As His goodness, His mercy, and His love are dwelt upon, clearer and still clearer will be the perception of truth; higher, holier, the desire for purity of heart and clearness of thought. The soul dwelling in the pure atmosphere of holy thought is transformed by intercourse with God through the study of His Word. Truth is so large, so far-reaching, so deep, so broad, that self is lost sight of. The heart is softened and subdued into humility, kindness, and love.

Happy Results of Bible Study

And the natural powers are enlarged because of holy obedience. From the study of the Word of life, students may come forth with minds expanded, elevated, ennobled. If they are, like Daniel, hearers and doers of the Word of God, they may advance as he did in all branches of learning. Being pure-minded, they will become strong-minded. Every intellectual faculty will be quickened. They may so educate and discipline themselves that all within the sphere of their influence shall see what man can be, and what he can do, when connected with the God of wisdom and power.

Our lifework here is a preparation for the life eternal. The education begun here will not be completed in this life; it will be going forward through all eternity—ever progressing, never completed. More and more fully will be revealed the wisdom and love of God in the plan of redemption. The Saviour, as He leads His children to the fountains of living waters, will impart rich stores of knowledge. And day by day the wonderful works of God, the evidences of His power in creating and sustaining the universe, will open before the mind in new beauty. In the light that shines from the throne, mysteries will disappear, and the soul will be filled with astonishment at the simplicity of the things that were never before comprehended.

Now we see through a glass, darkly; but then face to face; now we know in part; but then we shall know even as also we are known.

254

Everyday Religion

THERE is an eloquence far more powerful than the eloquence of words in the quiet, consistent life of a pure, true Christian. What a man is has more influence than what he says.

The officers who were sent to Jesus came back with the report that never man spoke as He spoke. But the reason for this was that never man lived as He lived. Had His life been other than it was, He could not have spoken as He did. His words bore with them a convincing power, because they came from a heart pure and holy, full of love and sympathy, benevolence and truth.

Influence on Others

It is our own character and experience that determine our influence upon others. In order to convince others of the power of Christ's grace, we must know its power in our own hearts and lives. The gospel we present for the saving of souls must be the gospel by which our own souls are saved. Only through a living faith in Christ as a personal Saviour is it possible to make our influence felt in a skeptical world. If we would draw sinners out of the swift-running current, our own feet must be firmly set upon the Rock, Christ Jesus.

The badge of Christianity is not an outward sign, not

the wearing of a cross or a crown, but it is that which reveals the union of man with God. By the power of His grace manifested in the transformation of character the world is to be convinced that God has sent His Son as its Redeemer. No other influence that can surround the human soul has such power as the influence of an unselfish life. The strongest argument in favor of the gospel is a loving and lovable Christian.

To live such a life, to exert such an influence, costs at every step, effort, self-sacrifice, discipline. It is because they do not understand this that many are so easily discouraged in the Christian life. Many who sincerely consecrate their lives to God's service are surprised and disappointed to find themselves, as never before, confronted by obstacles and beset by trials and perplexities. They pray for Christlikeness of character, for a fitness for the Lord's work, and they are placed in circumstances that seem to call forth all the evil of their nature. Faults are revealed of which they did not even suspect the existence. Like Israel of old, they question, If God is leading us, why do all these things come upon us?

Chosen Methods of Discipline

It is because God is leading them that these things come upon them. Trials and obstacles are the Lord's chosen methods of discipline and His appointed conditions of success. He who reads the hearts of men knows their characters better than they themselves know them. He sees that some have powers and susceptibilities which, rightly directed, might be used in the advancement of His work. In His providence He brings these persons into different positions and varied circumstances that they may discover in their char-

256

acter the defects which have been concealed from their own knowledge. He gives them opportunity to correct these defects and to fit themselves for His service. Often He permits the fires of affliction to assail them that they may be purified.

The fact that we are called upon to endure trial shows that the Lord Jesus sees in us something precious which He desires to develop. If He saw in us nothing whereby He might glorify His name, He would not spend time in refining us. He does not cast worthless stones into His furnace. It is valuable ore that He refines. The blacksmith puts the iron and steel into the fire that he may know what manner of metal they are. The Lord allows His chosen ones to be placed in the furnace of affliction to prove what temper they are of and whether they can be fashioned for His work.

The potter takes the clay and molds it according to his will. He kneads it and works it. He tears it apart and presses it together. He wets it and then dries it. He lets it lie for a while without touching it. When it is perfectly pliable, he continues the work of making of it a vessel. He forms it into shape, and on the wheel trims and polishes it. He dries it in the sun and bakes it in the oven. Thus it becomes a vessel fit for use. So the great Master Worker desires to mold and fashion us. And as the clay is in the hands of the potter, so are we to be in His hands. We are not to try to do the work of the potter. Our part is to yield ourselves to be molded by the Master Worker.

"Beloved, think it not strange concerning the fiery trial which is to try you, as though some strange thing happened unto you: but rejoice, inasmuch as ye are partakers of Christ's sufferings; that, when His glory shall be revealed, ye may be glad also with exceeding joy." 1 Peter 4:12, 13.

257

Learning the Song of Life

In the full light of day, and in hearing of the music of other voices, the caged bird will not sing the song that his master seeks to teach him. He learns a snatch of this, a trill of that, but never a separate and entire melody. But the master covers the cage, and places it where the bird will listen to the one song he is to sing. In the dark, he tries and tries again to sing that song until it is learned, and he breaks forth in perfect melody. Then the bird is brought forth, and ever after he can sing that song in the light. Thus God deals with His children. He has a song to teach us, and when we have learned it amid the shadows of affliction, we can sing it ever afterward.

Many are dissatisfied with their lifework. It may be that their surroundings are uncongenial; their time is occupied with commonplace work, when they think themselves capable of higher responsibilities; often their efforts seem to them to be unappreciated or fruitless; their future is uncertain.

Let us remember that while the work we have to do may not be our choice, it is to be accepted as God's choice for us. Whether pleasing or unpleasing, we are to do the duty that lies nearest. "Whatsoever thy hand findeth to do, do it with thy might; for there is no work, nor device, nor knowledge, nor wisdom, in the grave, whither thou goest." Ecclesiastes 9:10.

If the Lord desires us to bear a message to Nineveh, it will not be as pleasing to Him for us to go to Joppa or to Capernaum. He has reasons for sending us to the place toward which our feet have been directed. At that very place there may be someone in need of the help we can give. He who sent Philip to the Ethiopian counselor, Peter to the Roman centurion, and the little Israelitish maiden to the help of Naaman, the Syrian captain, sends men and women and youth today as His representatives to those in need of divine help and guidance.

Our plans are not always God's plans. He may see that it is best for us and for His cause to refuse our very best intentions, as He did in the case of David. But of one thing we may be assured, He will bless and use in the advancement of His cause those who sincerely devote themselves and all they have to His glory. If He sees it best not to grant their desires, He will counterbalance the refusal by giving them tokens of His love and entrusting to them another service.

When God's Plans Succeed

In His loving care and interest for us, often He who understands us better than we understand ourselves refuses to permit us selfishly to seek the gratification of our own ambition. He does not permit us to pass by the homely but sacred duties that lie next us. Often these duties afford the very training essential to prepare us for a higher work. Often our plans fail, that God's plans for us may succeed.

We are never called upon to make a real sacrifice for God. Many things He asks us to yield to Him, but in doing this we are but giving up that which hinders us in the heavenward way. Even when called upon to surrender those things which in themselves are good, we may be sure that God is thus working out for us some higher good.

In the future life, the mysteries that here have annoyed

259

and disappointed us will be made plain. We shall see that our seemingly unanswered prayers and disappointed hopes have been among our greatest blessings.

We are to look upon every duty, however humble, as sacred because it is a part of God's service. Our daily prayer should be: "Lord, help me to do my best. Teach me how to do better work. Give me energy and cheerfulness. Help me to bring into my service the loving ministry of the Saviour."

Consider the experience of Moses. The education he received in Egypt as the king's grandson and the prospective heir to the throne was very thorough. Nothing was neglected that was calculated to make him a wise man, as the Egyptians understood wisdom. He received the highest civil and military training. He felt that he was fully prepared for the work of delivering Israel from bondage. But God judged otherwise. His providence appointed Moses forty years of training in the wilderness as a keeper of sheep.

The Education of Moses

The education that Moses had received in Egypt was a help to him in many respects; but the most valuable preparation for his lifework was that which he received while employed as a shepherd. Moses was naturally of an impetuous spirit. In Egypt a successful military leader, and a favorite with the king and the nation, he had been accustomed to receiving praise and flattery. He had attracted the people to himself. He hoped to accomplish by his own powers the work of delivering Israel. Far different were the lessons he had to learn as God's representative. As he led his flocks through the wilds of the mountains and into the green pas-

260

tures of the valleys, he learned faith and meekness, patience, humility, and self-forgetfulness. He learned to care for the weak, to nurse the sick, to seek after the straying, to bear with the unruly, to tend the lambs, and to nurture the old and the feeble.

In this work, Moses was drawn nearer to the Chief Shepherd. He became closely united to the Holy One of Israel. No longer did he plan to do a great work. He sought to do faithfully as unto God the work committed to his charge. He recognized the presence of God in his surroundings. All nature spoke to him of the unseen One. He knew God as a personal God, and in meditating upon His character he grasped more and more fully the sense of His presence. He found refuge in the everlasting arms.

After this experience, Moses heard the call from heaven to exchange his shepherd's crook for the rod of authority; to leave his flock of sheep and take the leadership of Israel. The divine command found him self-distrustful, slow of speech, and timid. He was overwhelmed with a sense of his incapacity to be a mouthpiece for God. But he accepted the work, putting his whole trust in the Lord. The greatness of his mission called into exercise the best powers of his mind. God blessed his ready obedience, and he became eloquent, hopeful, self-possessed, fitted for the greatest work ever given to man. Of him it is written: "There hath not arisen a prophet since in Israel like unto Moses, whom Jehovah knew face to face." Deuteronomy 34:10, A.R.V.

Let those who feel that their work is not appreciated, and who crave a position of greater responsibility, consider that "promotion cometh neither from the east, nor from the west, nor from the south. But God is the Judge: He putteth down one, and setteth up another." Psalm 75:6, 7. Every man has his place in the eternal plan of heaven. Whether we fill that place depends upon our own faithfulness in co-operating with God.

We need to beware of self-pity. Never indulge the feeling that you are not esteemed as you should be, that your efforts are not appreciated, that your work is too difficult. Let the memory of what Christ has endured for us silence every murmuring thought. We are treated better than was our Lord. "Seekest thou great things for thyself? seek them not." Jeremiah 45:5. The Lord has no place in His work for those who have a greater desire to win the crown than to bear the cross. He wants men who are more intent upon doing their duty than upon receiving their reward—men who are more solicitous for principle than for promotion.

Those who are humble, and do their work as unto God, may not make so great a show as do those who are full of bustle and self-importance; but their work counts for more. Often those who make a great parade call attention to self, interposing between the people and God, and their work proves a failure. "Wisdom is the principal thing; therefore get wisdom: and with all thy getting get understanding. Exalt her, and she shall promote thee: she shall bring thee to honor, when thou dost embrace her." Proverbs 4:7, 8.

The Call to Come Up Higher

Because they have not the determination to take themselves in hand and to reform, many become stereotyped in a wrong course of action. But this need not be. They may cultivate their powers to do the very best kind of service, and then they will be always in demand. They will be valued for all that they are worth.

If any are qualified for a higher position, the Lord will lay the burden, not alone on them, but on those who have tested them, who know their worth, and who can understandingly urge them forward. It is those who perform faithfully their appointed work day by day, who in God's own time will hear His call, Come up higher.

While the shepherds were watching their flocks on the hills of Bethlehem, angels from heaven visited them. So today, while the humble worker for God is following his employment, angels of God stand by his side, listening to his words, noting the manner in which his work is done, to see if larger responsibilities may be entrusted to his hands.

Not by their wealth, their education, or their position does God estimate men. He estimates them by their purity of motive and their beauty of character. He looks to see how much of His Spirit they possess, and how much of His likeness their life reveals. To be great in God's kingdom is to be as a little child in humility, in simplicity of faith, and in purity of love.

"Ye know," Christ said, "that the rulers of the Gentiles lord it over them, and their great ones exercise authority over them. Not so shall it be among you: but whosoever would become great among you shall be your minister." Matthew 20:25, 26, R.V.

The Highest Honor

Of all the gifts that heaven can bestow upon men, fellowship with Christ in His sufferings is the most weighty trust and the highest honor. Not Enoch, who was trans-

263

lated to heaven, not Elijah, who ascended in a chariot of fire, was greater or more honored than John the Baptist, who perished alone in the dungeon. "Unto you it is given in the behalf of Christ, not only to believe on Him, but also to suffer for His sake." Philippians 1:29.

Many are unable to make definite plans for the future. Their life is unsettled. They cannot discern the outcome of affairs, and this often fills them with anxiety and unrest. Let us remember that the life of God's children in this world is a pilgrim life. We have not wisdom to plan our own lives. It is not for us to shape our future. "By faith Abraham, when he was called to go out into a place which he should after receive for an inheritance, obeyed; and he went out, not knowing whither he went." Hebrews 11:8.

Christ, in His life on earth, made no plans for Himself. He accepted God's plans for Him, and day by day the Father unfolded His plans. So should we depend upon God, that our lives may be the simple outworking of His will. As we commit our ways to Him, He will direct our steps.

Too many, in planning for a brilliant future, make an utter failure. Let God plan for you. As a little child, trust to the guidance of Him who will "keep the feet of His saints." 1 Samuel 2:9. God never leads His children otherwise than they would choose to be led if they could see the end from the beginning and discern the glory of the purpose which they are fulfilling as co-workers with Him.

When Christ called His disciples to follow Him, He offered them no flattering prospects in this life. He gave them no promise of gain or worldly honor, nor did they make any stipulation as to what they should receive. To Matthew as he sat at the receipt of custom, the Saviour said, "Follow

264

Me. And he left all, rose up, and followed Him." Luke 5:27, 28. Matthew did not, before rendering service, wait to demand a certain salary equal to the amount received in his former occupation. Without question or hesitation he followed Jesus. It was enough for him that he was to be with the Saviour, that he might hear His words and unite with Him in His work.

So it was with the disciples previously called. When Jesus bade Peter and his companions follow Him, immediately they left their boats and nets. Some of these disciples had friends dependent on them for support; but when they received the Saviour's invitation, they did not hesitate and inquire, How shall I live, and sustain my family? They were obedient to the call; and when afterward Jesus asked them, "When I sent you without purse, and scrip, and shoes, lacked ye anything?" they could answer, "Nothing." Luke 22:35.

A Complete Surrender to God

Today the Saviour calls us, as He called Matthew and John and Peter, to His work. If our hearts are touched by His love, the question of compensation will not be uppermost in our minds. We shall rejoice to be co-workers with Christ, and we shall not fear to trust His care. If we make God our strength, we shall have clear perceptions of duty, unselfish aspirations; our life will be actuated by a noble purpose which will raise us above sordid motives.

Many who profess to be Christ's followers have an anxious, troubled heart because they are afraid to trust themselves with God. They do not make a complete surrender to Him, for they shrink from the consequences that such a surrender may involve. Unless they do make this surrender, they cannot find peace.

There are many whose hearts are aching under a load of care because they seek to reach the world's standard. They have chosen its service, accepted its perplexities, adopted its customs. Thus their character is marred and their life made a weariness. The continual worry is wearing out the life forces. Our Lord desires them to lay aside this yoke of bondage. He invites them to accept His yoke; He says, "My yoke is easy, and My burden is light." Matthew 11:30. Worry is blind and cannot discern the future; but Jesus sees the end from the beginning. In every difficulty He has His way prepared to bring relief. "No good thing will He withhold from them that walk uprightly." Psalm 84:11.

Our heavenly Father has a thousand ways to provide for us of which we know nothing. Those who accept the one principle of making the service of God supreme will find perplexities vanish and a plain path before their feet.

The faithful discharge of today's duties is the best preparation for tomorrow's trials. Do not gather together all tomorrow's liabilities and cares and add them to the burden of today. "Sufficient unto the day is the evil thereof." Matthew 6:34.

His Power Is Absolute

Let us be hopeful and courageous. Despondency in God's service is sinful and unreasonable. He knows our every necessity. To the omnipotence of the King of kings our covenant-keeping God unites the gentleness and care of the tender shepherd. His power is absolute, and it is the pledge of the sure fulfillment of His promises to all who trust in Him.

He has means for the removal of every difficulty, that those who serve Him and respect the means He employs may be sustained. His love is as far above all other love as the heavens are above the earth. He watches over His children with a love that is measureless and everlasting.

In the darkest days, when appearances seem most forbidding, have faith in God. He is working out His will, doing all things well in behalf of His people. The strength of those who love and serve Him will be renewed day by day.

He is able and willing to bestow upon His servants all the help they need. He will give them the wisdom which their varied necessities demand.

Said the tried apostle Paul: "He said unto me, My grace is sufficent for thee: for My strength is made perfect in weakness. Most gladly therefore will I rather glory in my infirmities, that the power of Christ may rest upon me. Therefore I take pleasure in infirmities, in reproaches, in necessities, in persecutions, in distresses for Christ's sake: for when I am weak, then am I strong." 2 Corinthians 12:9, 10.

267

Living With Others

EVERY association of life calls for the exercise of self-control, forbearance, and sympathy. We differ so widely in disposition, habits, education, that our ways of looking at things vary. We judge differently. Our understanding of truth, our ideas in regard to the conduct of life, are not in all respects the same. There are no two whose experience is alike in every particular. The trials of one are not the trials of another. The duties that one finds light are to another most difficult and perplexing.

So frail, so ignorant, so liable to misconception is human nature, that each should be careful in the estimate he places upon another. We little know the bearing of our acts upon the experience of others. What we do or say may seem to us of little moment, when, could our eyes be opened, we should see that upon it depended the most important results for good or for evil.

Many have borne so few burdens, their hearts have known so little real anguish, they have felt so little perplexity and distress in behalf of others, that they cannot understand the work of the true burden bearer. No more capable are they of appreciating his burdens than is the child of understanding the care and toil of his burdened father. The child may wonder at his father's fears and perplexities. These appear needless to him. But when years of experience shall have been added to his life, when he himself comes to bear its burdens, he will look back upon his father's life and understand that which was once so incomprehensible. Bitter experience has given him knowledge.

The work of many a burden bearer is not understood, his labors are not appreciated, until death lays him low. When others take up the burdens he has laid down and meet the difficulties he encountered, they can understand how his faith and courage were tested. Often then the mistakes they were so quick to censure are lost sight of. Experience teaches them sympathy. God permits men to be placed in positions of responsibility. When they err, He has power to correct or to remove them. We should be careful not to take into our hands the work of judging that belongs to God.

The Saviour bids us, "Judge not, that ye be not judged. For with what judgment ye judge, ye shall be judged: and with what measure ye mete, it shall be measured to you again." Matthew 7:1, 2. Remember that soon your life record will pass in review before God. Remember, too, that He has said, "Thou art inexcusable, O man, whosoever thou art that judgest: . . . for thou that judgest doest the same things." Romans 2:1.

The Purpose of Life

We cannot afford to let our spirits chafe over any real or supposed wrong done to ourselves. Self is the enemy we most need to fear. No form of vice has a more baleful effect upon the character than has human passion not under the control of the Holy Spirit. No other victory we can gain will be so precious as the victory gained over self.

We should not allow our feelings to be easily wounded. We are to live, not to guard our feelings or our reputation, but to save souls. As we become interested in the salvation of souls, we cease to mind the little differences that so often arise in our association with one another. Whatever others may think of us or do to us, it need not disturb our oneness with Christ, the fellowship of the Spirit. "What glory is it, if, when ye be buffeted for your faults, ye shall take it patiently? but if, when ye do well, and suffer for it, ye take it patiently, this is acceptable with God." 1 Peter 2:20.

Do not retaliate. So far as you can do so, remove all cause for misapprehension. Avoid the appearance of evil. Do all that lies in your power, without the sacrifice of principle, to conciliate others. "If thou bring thy gift to the altar, and there rememberest that thy brother hath aught against thee; leave there thy gift before the altar, and go thy way; first be reconciled to thy brother, and then come and offer thy gift." Matthew 5:23, 24.

If impatient words are spoken to you, never reply in the same spirit. Remember that "a soft answer turneth away wrath." Proverbs 15:1. And there is wonderful power in silence. Words spoken in reply to one who is angry sometimes serve only to exasperate. But anger met with silence, in a tender, forbearing spirit, quickly dies away.

Under a storm of stinging, faultfinding words, keep the mind stayed upon the Word of God. Let mind and heart be stored with God's promises. If you are ill-treated or wrongfully accused, instead of returning an angry answer, repeat to yourself the precious promises:

"Be not overcome of evil, but overcome evil with good." Romans 12:21.

270

"Commit thy way unto the Lord; trust also in Him; and He shall bring it to pass. And He shall bring forth thy righteousness as the light, and thy judgment as the noonday." Psalm 37:5, 6.

"There is nothing covered, that shall not be revealed; neither hid, that shall not be known." Luke 12:2.

"Thou hast caused men to ride over our heads; we went through fire and through water: but Thou broughtest us out into a wealthy place." Psalm 66:12.

We are prone to look to our fellowmen for sympathy and uplifting, instead of looking to Jesus. In His mercy and faithfulness God often permits those in whom we place confidence to fail us, in order that we may learn the folly of trusting in man and making flesh our arm. Let us trust fully, humbly, unselfishly in God. He knows the sorrows that we feel to the depths of our being, but which we cannot express. When all things seem dark and unexplainable, remember the words of Christ, "What I do thou knowest not now; but thou shalt know hereafter." John 13:7.

A Noble Heroism

Study the history of Joseph and of Daniel. The Lord did not prevent the plottings of men who sought to do them harm; but He caused all these devices to work for good to His servants who amidst trial and conflict preserved their faith and loyalty.

So long as we are in the world we shall meet with adverse influences. There will be provocations to test the temper; and it is by meeting these in a right spirit that the Christian graces are developed. If Christ dwells in us, we shall be patient, kind, and forbearing, cheerful amid frets and irritations. Day by day and year by year we shall conquer self, and grow into a noble heroism. This is our allotted task; but it cannot be accomplished without help from Jesus, resolute decision, unwavering purpose, continual watchfulness, and unceasing prayer. Each one has a personal battle to fight. Not even God can make our characters noble or our lives useful, unless we become co-workers with Him. Those who decline the struggle lose the strength and joy of victory.

We need not keep our own record of trials and difficulties, griefs, and sorrow. All these things are written in the books, and heaven will take care of them. While we are counting up the disagreeable things, many things that are pleasant to reflect upon are passing from memory, such as the merciful kindness of God surrounding us every moment, and the love over which angels marvel, that God gave His Son to die for us.

The Unseen Realities

If you do not feel lighthearted and joyous, do not talk of your feelings. Cast no shadow upon the lives of others. A cold, sunless religion never draws souls to Christ. It drives them away from Him, into the nets that Satan has spread for the feet of the straying. Instead of thinking of your discouragements, think of the power you can claim in Christ's name. Let your imagination take hold upon things unseen. Let your thoughts be directed to the evidences of the great love of God for you. Faith can endure trial, resist temptation, bear up under disappointment. Jesus lives as our Advocate. All is ours that His mediation secures.

Think you not that Christ values those who live wholly for Him? Think you not that He visits those who, like the

272

beloved John in exile, are for His sake in hard and trying places? God will not suffer one of His truehearted workers to be left alone, to struggle against great odds and be overcome. He preserves as a precious jewel everyone whose life is hid with Christ in Him. Of every such one He says: "I . . . will make thee as a signet: for I have chosen thee." Haggai 2:23.

Talk of God's Promises

Then talk of the promises; talk of Jesus' willingness to bless. He does not forget us for one brief moment. When, notwithstanding disagreeable circumstances, we rest confidingly in His love and shut ourselves in with Him, the sense of His presence will inspire a deep, tranquil joy. Of Himself Christ said: "I do nothing of Myself; but as My Father hath taught Me, I speak these things. And He that sent Me is with Me: the Father hath not left Me alone; for I do always those things that please Him." John 8:28, 29.

The Father's presence encircled Christ, and nothing befell Him but that which infinite love permitted for the blessing of the world. Here was His source of comfort, and it is for us. He who is imbued with the Spirit of Christ abides in Christ. Whatever comes to him comes from the Saviour, who surrounds him with His presence. Nothing can touch him except by the Lord's permission. All our sufferings and sorrows, all our temptations and trials, all our sadness and griefs, all our persecutions and privations—in short, all things—work together for our good. All experiences and circumstances are God's workmen whereby good is brought to us.

If we have a sense of the long-suffering of God toward

273

us, we shall not be found judging or accusing others. When Christ was living on the earth, how surprised His associates would have been, if, after becoming acquainted with Him, they had heard Him speak one word of accusation, of fault-finding, or of impatience. Let us never forget that those who love Him are to represent Him in character.

"Be kindly affectioned one to another with brotherly love; in honor preferring one another." Romans 12:10. "Not rendering evil for evil, or railing for railing: but contrari-wise blessing; knowing that ye are thereunto called, that ye should inherit a blessing." 1 Peter 3:9.

Respecting Human Rights

The Lord Jesus demands our acknowledgment of the rights of every man. Men's social rights, and their rights as Christians, are to be taken into consideration. All are to be treated with refinement and delicacy, as the sons and daughters of God.

Christianity will make a man a gentleman. Christ was courteous, even to His persecutors; and His true followers will manifest the same spirit. Look at Paul when brought before rulers. His speech before Agrippa is an illustration of true courtesy as well as persuasive eloquence. The gospel does not encourage the formal politeness current with the world, but the courtesy that springs from real kindness of heart.

The most careful cultivation of the outward proprieties of life is not sufficient to shut out all fretfulness, harsh judg-ment, and unbecoming speech. True refinement will never be revealed so long as self is considered as the supreme object. Love must dwell in the heart. A thoroughgoing

274

Christian draws his motives of action from his deep heart love for his Master. Up through the roots of his affection for Christ springs an unselfish interest in his brethren. Love imparts to its possessor grace, propriety, and comeliness of deportment. It illuminates the countenance and subdues the voice; it refines and elevates the whole being.

Life is chiefly made up, not of great sacrifices and wonderful achievements, but of little things. It is oftenest through the little things which seem so unworthy of notice that great good or evil is brought into our lives. It is through our failure to endure the tests that come to us in little things that the habits are molded, the character misshaped; and when the greater tests come, they find us unready. Only by acting upon principle in the tests of daily life can we acquire power to stand firm and faithful in the most dangerous and most difficult positions.

We are never alone. Whether we choose Him or not, we have a companion. Remember that wherever you are, whatever you do, God is there. Nothing that is said or done or thought can escape His attention. To your every word or deed you have a witness—the holy, sin-hating God. Before you speak or act, always think of this. As a Christian, you are a member of the royal family, a child of the heavenly King. Say no word, do no act, that shall bring dishonor upon "that worthy name by the which ye are called." James 2:7.

What Would Jesus Do?

Study carefully the divine-human character, and constantly inquire, "What would Jesus do were He in my place?" This should be the measurement of our duty. Do not place yourselves needlessly in the society of those who by their arts would weaken your purpose to do right or bring a stain upon your conscience. Do nothing among strangers, in the street, on the cars, in the home, that would have the least appearance of evil. Do something every day to improve, beautify, and ennoble the life that Christ has purchased with His own blood.

Always act from principle, never from impulse. Temper the natural impetuosity of your nature with meekness and gentleness. Indulge in no lightness or trifling. Let no low witticism escape your lips. Even the thoughts are not to be allowed to run riot. They must be restrained, brought into captivity to the obedience of Christ. Let them be placed upon holy things. Then, through the grace of Christ, they will be pure and true.

Power of Pure Thoughts

We need a constant sense of the ennobling power of pure thoughts. The only security for any soul is right thinking. As a man "thinketh in his heart, so is he." Proverbs 23:7. The power of self-restraint strengthens by exercise. That which at first seems difficult, by constant repetition grows easy, until right thoughts and actions become habitual. If we will, we may turn away from all that is cheap and inferior, and rise to a high standard; we may be respected by men and be loved of God.

Cultivate the habit of speaking well of others. Dwell upon the good qualities of those with whom you associate, and see as little as possible of their errors and failings. When tempted to complain of what someone has said or done, praise something in that person's life or character. Cultivate thankfulness. Praise God for His wonderful love in giving Christ to die for us. It never pays to think of our grievances. God calls upon us to think of His mercy and His matchless love, that we may be inspired with praise.

Earnest workers have no time for dwelling upon the faults of others. We cannot afford to live on the husks of others' faults or failings. Evil speaking is a twofold curse, falling more heavily upon the speaker than upon the hearer. He who scatters the seeds of dissension and strife, reaps in his own soul the deadly fruits. The very act of looking for evil in others develops evil in those who look. By dwelling upon the faults of others, we are changed into the same image. But by beholding Jesus, talking of His love and perfection of character, we become changed into His image. By contemplating the lofty ideal He has placed before us, we shall be uplifted into a pure and holy atmosphere, even the presence of God. When we abide here, there goes forth from us a light that irradiates all who are connected with us.

A Source of Strength to Others

Instead of criticizing and condemning others, say: "I must work out my own salvation. If I cooperate with Him who desires to save my soul, I must watch myself diligently. I must put away every evil from my life. I must overcome every fault. I must become a new creature in Christ. Then, instead of weakening those who are striving against evil, I can strengthen them by encouraging words." We are too indifferent in regard to one another. Too often we forget that our fellow laborers are in need of strength and cheer. Take care to assure them of your interest and sympathy. Help them by your prayers, and let them know that you do it.

All who profess to be children of God should bear in mind that as missionaries they will be brought into contact with all classes of minds. There are the refined and the coarse, the humble and the proud, the religious and the skeptical, the educated and the ignorant, the rich and the poor. These varied minds cannot be treated alike; yet all need kindness and sympathy. By mutual contact our minds should receive polish and refinement. We are dependent upon one another, closely bound together by the ties of human brotherhood.

It is through the social relations that Christianity comes in contact with the world. Every man or woman who has received the divine illumination is to shed light on the dark pathway of those who are unacquainted with the better way. Social power, sanctified by the Spirit of Christ, must be improved in bringing souls to the Saviour. Christ is not to be hid away in the heart as a coveted treasure, sacred and sweet, to be enjoyed solely by the possessor. We are to have Christ in us as a well of water, springing up into everlasting life, refreshing all who come in contact with us.

The Highest Experience

WE NEED constantly a fresh revelation of Christ, a daily experience that harmonizes with His teachings. High and holy attainments are within our reach. Continual progress in knowledge and virtue is God's purpose for us. His law is the echo of His own voice, giving to all the invitation, "Come up higher. Be holy, holier still." Every day we may advance in perfection of Christian character.

Many who are already members of God's great family know little of what it means to behold His glory and to be changed from glory to glory. Many have a twilight perception of Christ's excellence, and their hearts thrill with joy. They long for a fuller, deeper sense of the Saviour's love. Let these cherish every desire of the soul after God. The Holy Spirit works with those who will be worked, molds those who will be molded, fashions those who will be fashioned. Give yourselves the culture of spiritual thoughts and holy communings. You have seen but the first rays of the early dawn of His glory. As you follow on to know the Lord, you will know that "the path of the righteous is as the light of dawn, that shineth more and more unto the perfect day." Proverbs 4:18, R.V., margin.

"These things have I spoken unto you," said Christ, "that My joy might remain in you, and that your joy might be full." John 15:11.

Restoring the Image of God

Ever before Him, Christ saw the result of His mission. His earthly life, so full of toil and self-sacrifice, was cheered by the thought that He would not have all this travail for nought. By giving His life for the life of men, He would restore in humanity the image of God. He would lift us up from the dust, reshape the character after the pattern of His own character, and make it beautiful with His own glory.

Christ saw of the travail of His soul and was satisfied. He viewed the expanse of eternity, and saw the happiness of those who through His humiliation should receive pardon and everlasting life. He was wounded for their transgressions, bruised for their iniquities. The chastisement of their peace was upon Him, and with His stripes they were healed. He heard the shout of the redeemed. He heard the ransomed ones singing the song of Moses and the Lamb. Although the baptism of blood must first be received, although the sins of the world were to weigh upon His innocent soul, although the shadow of an unspeakable woe was upon Him; yet for the joy that was set before Him He chose to endure the cross, and despised the shame.

This joy all His followers are to share. However great and glorious hereafter, our reward is not all to be reserved for the time of final deliverance. Even here we are by faith to enter into the Saviour's joy. Like Moses, we are to endure as seeing the Invisible.

Now the church is militant. Now we are confronted with a world in darkness, almost wholly given over to idolatry. But the day is coming when the battle will have been fought, the victory won. The will of God is to be done on earth as it is done in heaven. The nations of the saved will know no other law than the law of heaven. All will be a happy, united family, clothed with the garments of praise and thanksgiving—the robe of Christ's righteousness. All nature, in its surpassing loveliness, will offer to God a tribute of praise and adoration. The world will be bathed in the light of heaven. The light of the moon will be as the light of the sun, and the light of the sun will be sevenfold greater than it is now. The years will move on in gladness. Over the scene the morning stars will sing together, and the sons of God will shout for joy, while God and Christ will unite in proclaiming, There shall be no more sin, neither shall there be any more death.

We need to keep ever before us this vision of things unseen. It is thus that we shall be able to set a right value on the things of eternity and the things of time. It is this that will give us power to influence others for the higher life.

"Come up unto Me into the mount," God bids us. To Moses, before he could be God's instrument in delivering Israel, was appointed the forty years of communion with Him in the mountain solitudes. Before bearing God's message to Pharaoh, he spoke with the angel in the burning bush. Before receiving God's law as the representative of His people, he was called into the mount and beheld His glory. Before executing justice on the idolaters, he was hidden in the cleft of the rock, and the Lord said, "I will proclaim the name of the Lord before thee," "merciful and gracious, slow to anger, and abundant in loving-kindness and truth; . . . and that will by no means clear the guilty." Exodus 33:19; 34:6, 7, A.R.V. Before he laid down, with his life, his burden for Israel, God called him to the top of Pisgah, and spread out before him the glory of the Promised Land.

In the Mount With Jesus

Before the disciples went forth on their mission, they were called up into the mount with Jesus. Before the power and glory of Pentecost, came the night of communion with the Saviour, the meeting on the mountain in Galilee, the parting scene upon Olivet, with the angels' promise, and the days of prayer and communion in the upper chamber.

Jesus, when preparing for some great trial or some important work, would resort to the solitude of the mountains, and spend the night in prayer to His Father. A night of prayer preceded the ordination of the apostles and the Sermon on the Mount, the transfiguration, the agony of the judgment hall and the cross, and the resurrection glory.

We, too, must have times set apart for meditation and prayer and for receiving spiritual refreshing. We do not value the power and efficacy of prayer as we should. Prayer and faith will do what no power on earth can accomplish. We are seldom, in all respects, placed in the same position twice. We continually have new scenes and new trials to pass through, where past experience cannot be a sufficient guide. We must have the continual light that comes from God.

Christ is ever sending messages to those who listen for His voice. On the night of the agony in Gethsemane, the sleeping disciples heard not the voice of Jesus. They had a dim sense of the angel's presence, but lost the power and glory of the scene. Because of their drowsiness and stupor, they failed of receiving the evidence that would have strengthened their souls for the terrible scenes before them. Thus today the very men who most need divine instruction often fail of receiving it, because they do not place themselves in communion with Heaven.

The temptations to which we are daily exposed make prayer a necessity. Dangers beset every path. Those who are seeking to rescue others from vice and ruin are especially exposed to temptation. In constant contact with evil, they need a strong hold upon God, lest they themselves be corrupted. Short and decisive are the steps that lead men down from high and holy ground to a low level. In a moment decisions may be made that fix one's condition forever. One failure to overcome leaves the soul unguarded. One evil habit, if not firmly resisted, will strengthen into chains of steel, binding the whole man.

Men and Women of Prayer

The reason why so many are left to themselves in places of temptation is that they do not set the Lord always before them. When we permit our communion with God to be broken, our defense is departed from us. Not all your good purposes and good intentions will enable you to withstand evil. You must be men and women of prayer. Your petitions must not be faint, occasional, and fitful, but earnest, persevering, and constant. It is not always necessary to bow upon your knees in order to pray. Cultivate the habit of talking with the Saviour when you are alone, when you are walking, and when you are busy with your daily labor. Let the heart be continually uplifted in silent petition for help, for light, for strength, for knowledge. Let every breath be a prayer.

We shall not be put to shame if we make God our trust. Christ in the heart, Christ in the life—this is our safety. The atmosphere of His presence will fill the soul with abhorrence of all that is evil. Our spirit may be so identified with His that in thought and aim we shall be one with Him.

It was through faith and prayer that Jacob, from being a man of feebleness and sin, became a prince with God. It is thus that you may become men and women of high and holy purpose, of noble life, men and women who will not for any consideration be swayed from truth, right, and justice. All are pressed with urgent cares, burdens, and duties, but the more difficult your position and the heavier your burdens, the more you need Jesus.

The Privilege of Divine Worship

It is a serious mistake to neglect the public worship of God. The privileges of divine service should not be lightly regarded. Those who attend upon the sick are often unable to avail themselves of these privileges, but they should be careful not to absent themselves needlessly from the house of worship.

We must live a twofold life—a life of thought and action, of silent prayer and earnest work. The strength received through communion with God, united with earnest effort in training the mind to thoughtfulness and care-taking, prepares one for daily duties, and keeps the spirit in peace under all circumstances, however trying.

When in trouble, many think they must appeal to some earthly friend, telling him their perplexities, and begging for help. Under trying circumstances unbelief fills their hearts, and the way seems dark. And all the time there stands beside them the mighty Counselor of the ages, inviting them to place their confidence in Him. Jesus, the great Burden Bearer, is saying, "Come unto Me, . . . and I will give you rest." Shall we turn from Him to uncertain human beings, who are as dependent upon God as we ourselves are?

You may feel the deficiency of your character, and the smallness of your ability, in comparison with the greatness of the work. But if you had the greatest intellect ever given to man, it would not be sufficient for your work. "Without Me ye can do nothing," says our Lord and Saviour. John 15:5. The result of all we do rests in the hands of God. Whatever may betide, lay hold upon Him with steady, persevering confidence.

In your business, in companionship for leisure hours, and in alliance for life, let all the associations you form be entered upon with earnest, humble prayer. You will thus show that you honor God, and God will honor you. Pray when you are fainthearted. When you are desponding, close the lips firmly to men; do not shadow the path of others; but tell everything to Jesus. Reach up your hands for help. In your weakness, lay hold of infinite strength. Ask for humility, wisdom, courage, increase of faith, that you may see light in God's light, and rejoice in His love.

Still Greater Blessings

When we are humble and contrite, we stand where God can and will manifest Himself to us. He is well pleased when we urge past mercies and blessings as a reason why He should bestow on us greater blessings. He will more than fulfill the expectations of those who trust fully in Him. The Lord Jesus knows just what His children need, how much divine power we will appropriate for the blessing of humanity; and He bestows upon us all that we will employ in blessing others and ennobling our own souls.

We must have less trust in what we ourselves can do, and more trust in what the Lord can do for and through us. You are not engaged in your own work; you are doing the work of God. Surrender your will and way to Him. Make not a single reserve, not a single compromise with self. Know what it is to be free in Christ.

The mere hearing of sermons Sabbath after Sabbath, the reading of the Bible through and through, or the explanation of it verse by verse, will not benefit us or those who hear us, unless we bring the truths of the Bible into our individual experience. The understanding, the will, the affections, must be yielded to the control of the Word of God. Then through the work of the Holy Spirit the precepts of the Word will become the principles of the life.

As you ask the Lord to help you, honor your Saviour by believing that you do receive His blessing. All power, all wisdom, are at our command. We have only to ask.

Walk in the Light of God

Walk continually in the light of God. Meditate day and night upon His character. Then you will see His beauty and rejoice in His goodness. Your heart will glow with a sense of His love. You will be uplifted, as if borne by everlasting arms. With the power and light that God imparts, you can comprehend more and accomplish more than you ever before deemed possible.

He whose trust is in God will with Paul be able to say, "I can do all things through Christ which strengtheneth me."

286

Philippians 4:13. Whatever the mistakes or failures of the past, we may, with the help of God, rise above them. With the apostle we may say:

"This one thing I do, forgetting those things which are behind, and reaching forth unto those things which are before, I press toward the mark for the prize of the high calling of God in Christ Jesus." Philippians 3:13, 14.

Index

ADJUSTMENTS in marriage 14, 15
Afflictions 256-258
Air, pure, need of 2
Alcohol, effects of 99-103
All things work together for good 273
Angels, ministry of 226, 244
Anger met with silence 270
Animals, for food 80-82
Appearance of evil 276
Appetite, bonds of 117, 118
educate and control 35, 36, 103
Association, influence of 52, 53
Associations to be made only after prayer 285
Athletic training 2

BATHING, daily 66
Battle and march, life is 243
Beauty, earth's, marred 228
God loves 228, 229
Between meals, eating 74
Bible, foundation of study 51
power of 248
Bird learns song in dark 258
Blessings through Christ 239
Blood, good, and pure air 63
Brain and stomach 76
Bread, religion in loaf of 73
of superfine white flour 72
Breathing, deep 63, 64, 154
Burden of sin 204

CANCEROUS germs in flesh 81
Caste, religion and 169, 170
Character, and influence 255
building 242
of God, Christ and 248
Cheerfulness, health and 38
Child, early training of 31-32
Childhood of Jesus 189
Children, activity of 46
and Jesus 178-180
not to be turned away by coldness 182
parents and 5, 24-29, 39-44
teach joy of Christ's service to 182

Choice, power of 117, 219
Christ, satisfied with results of travail 280
the wellspring of life 143
unseen in our streets 226
Christ's mission 164
Christian life, battle and march 243
Christianity will make gentleman 274
Circle, sacred, around family 15
Cities, and sick 152, 153
evils in 18, 19
Clothing needed 91, 92, 95
Communion with God 191, 192
results of lack of 282, 283
Community and true home 8
Companionship, children love 39
Conciliate others 270
Condiments and stomach 96
Confession, proper form of 159
Cooking, importance of 73, 74
Country life, for sick 151-155
Courage, talk 122
Creation, of man 231
not explained by science 230
Crime taught by reading 57

DAILY need of Christ 246, 247
Demoniacs of Gergesa 220-222
Dependence upon God 185, 186
Despair, none need 145
Despondency is sinful 266
Diet, care in reform of 86-89
children's 34-36
desire for rich 70
effects of flesh 83, 84
God's original 68-69
importance of mother's 26
individual 69
proper, need of 2
without flesh 71, 84, 85
Difficulty, removal of 267
Discouragement, song a weapon against 148
Disease, cause of 127-129
definition of 1
in food animals 81-83
Display of no value 177

289

Divine power, how much we can use 285, 286
Dress, and illness 96
children's 33, 34
Duties, afford training 259
children to be taught 44, 45
Duty, humble 258-260

EATING, and drinking, wrong habits of 102, 103, 129
habits 74, 75
regularity in 74
Education, health, needed 1
through eternity 254
true 48-53
Eloquence of life of true Christian 255
Emotions, do not study 145
Eternity before us 244
Evangelist, Christ as 167, 168
Evil speaking, curse of 277
Exercise, for regaining health 95, 133
in open air 154
need of 2, 130-133
Experimental knowledge of God by faith 249, 250
Extremes, diet reform should avoid 87-89

FAINTHEARTED, pray when 285
Fairy tales, myths, etc. 58, 59
Faith, connects us with heaven 199
in darkest days 267
mightier than death 197
saving, a transaction 197
strengthened by exercise 161
the centurion's 197-199
the cripple's 211-213
the leper's 201, 202
the paralytic's 205-207
the touch of 194-197
true 197
Families, society composed of 6
Family worship 42, 43
Fashion, and display 90, 91
device of adversary 93, 94

Faults of others 277
Feelings not to be easily wounded 270
Fellowship with Christ 263
Fiction reading 58
Fish and disease 82, 83
Flesh, before Flood 80
restricted in Israel 80, 81
secondhand food 81
Flesh diet, effects of 83, 84
Flour, superfine white 72
Food, choosing best 68, 69
dependence of body on 68
for Sabbath 77
ill-cooked 72, 73
Foods to be avoided 75
Fruit, with vegetables 71, 72
canning and drying of 71
Furnace of affliction 257
Future, plans for 264

GENTLEMAN, Christianity will make 274
Glory, God's, in nature 228
God's leading 264
Good deeds, a blessing 149
Good qualities, dwell on 276
Gospel, a living force 222
importance of, in the life 18
Gratitude promotes health 146
Grief, antidote to 144
Guests, provision for 9
Guilt, great 216

HABIT, evil 283
Handiwork, God's 230
Healing, Christ and 166, 213
Healing balm, in Christ 156
Healing power, Christ's 164, 165
Health, and good blood 63
obedience to laws of 2
regained by exercise 95
Healthful cookery 73, 74
Helping needy 149, 150
Hereditary and cultivated traits to be overcome 243
Highest education 247
History and prophecy 56, 57
Holiness of heart 253

Home, child's first school 50
  Christian 8
  conditions in Jesus' 20
  man's original 19, 20, 151
  true, and community 8
Homes, expensive 21, 22
  furnishings of 22, 23
  refuge for youth 9
  value of country 18-22
Homelife, importance of 6-10
  of Jesus 6
Hope in Christ 114, 115
Humanity, Christ one with 238
Humble, God manifest to 285
  work of the 262
  worker, angels help 263
Husband, responsibilities of
  26-29, 41-45

IMAGE of God restored 280
Imagination and disease 137
Impatient words, never use 270
Impulse, must not act from 242
Inactivity 130-132
Individuality, one's own 16
Indulgence, unhealthful 3
Infidel authors 55
Influence, of character 255
  of unselfish life 256
  on the skeptical 255
Influences, adverse 271
Intemperance from wrong food
  102, 103
Intemperate, hope for 113-122

JOHN THE BAPTIST and
      Christ's mission 175, 176
Joy, share Christ's 280
  in unselfish service 17
Judging, work of, is God's 269

KINGLY power of reason 4
Knowledge, Christ imparted only
  useful 59, 60
Knowledge of God, Christ gave
  clearer 236
  foundation of education 227
  through personal experience
  249, 250

to be given to children 249
  will re-create soul 240

LABOR troubles 18
Law of God, claims of 121
Laws of health, obedience to
  117, 118
  disregard of 127-129
  in sickroom 134
  know and obey 1
Laws of nature 231, 232
Leprosy, symbol of sin 200, 203
Life-giving properties in fra-
  grance of trees 153
Lifework and eternal life 254
Light of the world, Christ's
      followers to be 177
Liquor, evils of 105-112
Little things, life's 275
Loom of heaven, weaving of 17
Love, Christ's great 205
  cultivate mutual 15
  expression of 15
  God's, centers in cross 239
  golden bonds of 17
  not exchange of flattery 17
  power of Christ's 125
Lungs, function of 63, 64
Luxuries not promised 185

MARRIAGE, early 12
  preparation for 12-14
  safe only in Christ 13
  sanctioned by Christ 11
  symbol of union between
      Christ and redeemed 11
Master Artist, nature and 228
Meals, for Sabbath 77
  should be varied 72
  two a day 75, 88
Mechanism of human body 233
Meditation and prayer 271, 272
Melancholy 146
Mental depression 137
Mental powers, develop 61
Milk and eggs 87, 88
Milk and sugar together 72
Mind, controlling mind 139
  to be disciplined 243

291

uplifted by Bible 248
cure, danger of 137, 138
Minds expanded by Word 254
Missionary, every true disciple
is 224, 225
Modesty in dress 90, 91
Money wasted on display 90, 91
Moses, education of 260, 261
Mother, Jesus', His first
teacher 49
no other work equals that of
29, 30
preparation of 30
responsibilities of 25-29, 39-45
Mothers, Christ helps 181
Mysteries, made plain 259, 260

NATURAL laws, use 162, 163
Natural remedies 2
Nature, and Written Word 251
God works through 123
God's physician 153
testifies of God 228
used by Jesus to teach 191
Nature of God revealed in Christ
235, 236
Nervous excitement, effect of, on
children 32, 33
No time to lose 244
Nurse, physical vigor of 134
Nut foods, use of 70

OBEDIENCE, blessing of 124,
125
brings liberty 5
Olives, use of 70
Outdoor life, for invalids 151-155
Jesus lived 189
Overeating, results of 76-78
Overwork and sickness 129

PARENTS, children and 7, 12
duties of, in habit forming 8
first duty of 46, 47
influence of, on children 5,
24-28, 39-45
sacred trust committed to 12
Passions and the will 4
Patent medicines 128

Perfection of character 279
Perils surround us 245
Personal being, God is 229,
234-236
Pharisees, religion of 174, 175
Philosophical speculation 54
Philosophies, human 253
Philosophy, study God's 248
Physician, Christ as 156
Physician should direct sick to
God 139, 140
Physiology, children and 37, 38
Plans, ours and God's 259
Poor, needs of 90
Power, Christ's life of 188
God's, in nature 229, 232-234
of Christ's words 254
of God, talk of 148
Powers, higher, to rule 4
Practical training 51, 61
Praise, educate lips for 147
Prayer, answers to 161
Christ and 191, 192
for afflicted 149
for sick 158-163
may be presumption 158
to include "Thy will be
done" 160
let every breath be 283
Preexisting matter, God not
indebted to 231
Prenatal influences 25-28
Principle, act from 275-276
Promises, talk of 273
Pure-minded 254

QUESTION, all-important,
"What think ye of Christ?"
246
to study, "What is truth?" 246

REFINEMENT, true 274, 275
Reform, law of God and 3
need of divine power for 4
Regularity in eating 74
Religion, children and 182
cold, sunless 272
in loaf of bread 73
Remedial agencies 162, 163

Rest, need of 2
Restoration from sin 241
Retaliate, do not 270
Rich, Christ and 169
Riches, imperishable 178
Rights of every man 274
Romance, disappearance of 14
Royal family, Christian is
    member of 275
Rule of life, Christ's 225

SACRIFICE, real 269
Safety, Christ is our 284
Samaritans, Jesus and 171, 172
School, life is 18
Science, of Christianity 243
    true, and Word 251
Scripture, Christ and 167
Sedentary workers 78, 79, 133
Self, our enemy 269
Self-assertion, Jesus avoided 174,
    175
Self-control, children to be taught
    37, 38
Self-deceived, man's greatest
    danger is being 245
Self-indulgence and disease 158
Self-mastery, duty of 4
Self-pity, beware of 262
Self-sacrifice, Christ's 165, 166
Self-trust, renounce 245
Sensational stories 57
Sermon, true home as 8
Sickness, children's 36, 37
Sickness the work of Satan 123
Sickroom, Christ in 157
    conditions of 135
Simplicity, lesson of 183, 184
Sin, a tremendous evil 241
    confession of, before prayer
      for sick 158, 159
    darkens mind 253
    from neglecting Word 248
    leprosy as a symbol 203
    the heaviest burden 204
Skepticism, effects of 54
Social power 278
Social relations 278
Song, express praise in 148

Sons of God, Christ gives power
    to become 237
Soul transformed through study
    of Word 253
Stomach and brain 76
Strongest gospel argument 256
Student, take Bible 253
Study of Word 251-254
Study revelations of God 228
Sugar, use of 71, 72
Sunlight, need of 2, 65, 66
Surrender, complete 265, 266
Swine, flesh of 82
Sympathies 9

TEA and coffee 96, 97
Teacher, Christ as 168
Temperance in eating 78, 79
Temptations and prayer 283
Theory, dwelling on 246
Thinking, right 276
Thoughts to be restrained 276
Thousand ways, Father has 266
"Thy will be done" in prayer for
    sick 160
Tobacco, effects of 96-98
"Touch not, taste not, handle not"
    104
Traits to be overcome 243
Trials and difficulties 272
Trials and perplexities 256, 257
Trials, tomorrow's 266
True knowledge of ourselves, we
    must have 245
Trust, have less in self 286
    in God, need of 2
Trusting man, folly of 270
Twilight perception of Christ's
    excellence 279

UNCLEANLINESS and disease
    66, 67
Unity between Father and Son
    237-239
Uplifting fallen soul, greater
    miracle than healing 216

VEGETABLES and fruit not at
    same meal 71, 72

Ventilation, of sickroom 135
    proper 64, 65
Vice, cities hotbeds of 18
    remedy of 120
Victims of bad habits 7
Visiting the sick 136
Vital force 127, 128

WALK in the light of God 286
Water for health 129, 130
Wedlock, real union of 14
Will, Christ and Father's 165
    do not yield to another 138
    exercise of 141
    must be yielded to Word 286
    true force of 116, 117, 141

Wine and strong drink, sin for
    mother to take 26
Wine of Cana 101, 102
Word of God, Christ and 167
    food of mind and soul 250
    neglecting 248
    results of studying 251-254
Work, light, for patients 154
Worry, folly of 266
Worship, public 284
Wrongs, not to chafe over 269

YOUTH, development of 47, 48
    society and 7

ZWIEBACK, value of 72

294